ACKNOWLEDGEMENTS

BSRIA would like to thank the following sponsors for their contributions to this Guide:

Department of Trade and Industry
CIBSE (Chartered Institution of Building Services Engineers)
ACE (Association of Consulting Engineers)
ESTTL (Engineering Services Training Trust Limited)
HVCA (Heating and Ventilating Contractors Association)
Bovis
Crown House Engineering
FaberMaunsell
Hoare Lea
N G Bailey
South Bank University
Troup Bywaters & Anders
W S Atkins

The research project was undertaken under the guidance of a project steering group drawn from industry representatives and BSRIA staff. The steering group contributors were:

Fulcrum Consulting	Andrew Ford, representing DTI
Independent chair	Bryan Franklin
CIBSE	Hywel Davies
ACE	Jeremy Croxson
Bovis	Jean-Louis Auguste
Crown House Engineering	Susan Hone-Brookes
ESTTL	Tony Barton
FaberMaunsell	Quinten Babcock
	Ant Wilson
Hoare Lea	Graham Cossons
	Les Mackenzie
	Terry Wyatt
HVCA	Derrick Newson
	Bob Towse
N G Bailey	Ken Sargeant
	Roland Edkins
South Bank University	Martin Ratcliffe
Troup Bywaters & Anders	David Arnold (representing CIBSE)
W S Atkins	Adrian Defalco
	Steve Platt

Gay Lawrence Race and Sally Mitchell contributed from BSRIA.

This publication has been produced by BSRIA as part of a contract placed by the Department of Trade & Industry. The contract was let under the Partners in Innovation programme, which provides part funding of collaborative research. Any views expressed in it are not necessarily those of the Department.

The authors have sought to incorporate the views of the steering group, but final editorial control of this document rested with BSRIA.

©BSRIA 70186   June 2003   ISBN 0 86022 618 2   Printed by The Chameleon Press Ltd.

PREFACE

This publication provides practical, easy to follow methodologies for a range of calculations used in the design of heating ventilating and air conditioning building services systems.

The calculation sheets are presented in four sections covering:

- Heating loads and plant
- Cooling loads and plant
- Water flow distribution systems
- Air flow distribution systems

The calculation sheets provide practical guidance including design watchpoints, design tips and rules of thumb, and are intended to aid the design process and reduce errors. The guidance is based primarily on data and procedures contained within the *CIBSE Guides*, together with other sources such as *Building Regulations*, with clear cross-referencing provided to data sources.

This publication is intended primarily to help junior design engineers, working within a structured and supervised training framework, by providing assistance in completing the basic calculations needed to define operating conditions for systems, size distribution systems and to specify required duties for plant and equipment. It is not the purpose of this guide to identify the most appropriate system for a particular application. Such decisions require knowledge, experience and analysis of the application.

This guidance is also not intended to be exhaustive or definitive. It will be necessary for users to exercise their own professional judgement, or obtain further advice from senior engineers within their organisation when deciding whether to abide by or depart from the guide. The calculation sheets are relevant to many design applications, but cannot be fully comprehensive or cover every possible design scenario. Every design project is different and has differing needs, and it is the professional duty of the responsible design engineer to consider fully all design requirements. Designers should exercise professional judgement to decide relevant factors and establish the most appropriate data sources and methodologies to use for a particular application.

Designers must be aware of their contractual obligations and ensure that these are met. Following this guidance – or any other guidance – does not preclude or imply compliance with those obligations. Similarly, it is the duty of the designer to ensure compliance with all relevant legislation and regulations.

It is hoped that design practices and individual designers will be encouraged to share knowledge and experience by extending and adding to the design watchpoints and design tips, and disseminating this work within their organisations. BSRIA would be pleased to receive any such contributions for incorporation into any future revisions of this publication to provide wider industry sharing of such knowledge.

CONTENTS

Page

INTRODUCTION

BSRIA has been researching into the design process and design methodology in the building services industry since the mid 1990's. This has produced guidance on the use of engineering design margins[1], feedback to design[2] and quality control systems for detailed technical design[3]. The overall aim has been to develop systematic guidance for the industry that would contribute to greater consistency in design and to an overall raising of design standards.

The studies have involved considerable discussions with industrial partners on their current and future needs, and several visits to the design offices of a number of industrial contributors to the projects. A majority of those organisations consulted said that a lack of formal design guidance and inadequate recording of calculations was a major barrier to quality improvement in design. Many also felt that standardised formal procedures would help improve the quality of design outputs.

BSRIA's research also revealed that there is a lack of standardisation in design procedures, both between companies and between individuals. Many companies have developed their own design guidance and approaches to calculation procedures, leading to considerable diversity within the industry. This can make it difficult to cross-check work done by others, which could lead to differences in system design parameters and sizes, and even calculation and design errors. There are many specific examples of design errors and issues that should have been considered during design calculations and have led, (or could have led) to operational problems or subsequent litigation[4], including:

- Omission of HEPA filter resistance from fan-pressure calculations, requiring subsequent fan motor replacement which then required additional silencing
- Omission of duct sizes and flows from drawings, leading to incorrect sizes being installed
- Incorrect pipe and pump sizing for a constant temperature heating circuit, necessitating replacement of system distribution network
- No allowance for pipework expansion on a heating mains.

Although there is considerable design guidance and data available to inform the design process much of it is intended for use by experienced engineers, who have fulfilled a programme of education and training and have design experience. For example, while the design guides published by the Chartered Institution of Building Services Engineers (CIBSE)[5] provide essential design data for building services engineers, they are intended for use by experienced engineers, and therefore do not always show how to design in detail by giving every necessary calculation step. They also do not show how different calculation routines link together to build up the design process.

Research has also shown that many employers are currently finding it difficult to recruit design engineers with appropriate building services skills and experience, which necessitates recruiting and retraining engineers from other disciplines.[6] Output from building services courses is currently falling,[7] which implies there will be no short term improvement in this situation.

These recruits, with no building services training or experience, will require close supervision and considerable training which can place a heavy burden on company resources.

While there is no substitute for an appropriate quality control framework and adequate supervision by qualified senior staff, good training resources and technical support can provide an invaluable adjunct to company training provision.

Aim
As a result of all these factors many of the leading organisations involved in education and training in the building services industry, including BSRIA, CIBSE, ESTTL and HVCA and a number of industrial contributors embarked on this project to develop simple and clear guidance on building services calculation procedures that would be applicable across the industry.

Objectives
The resulting guidance is intended to be suitable as an in-company learning resource, in order to improve quality and communication within the design process. This should reduce the risk of design calculation errors and omissions, simplify the task of calculation checks and improve the overall efficiency of the design process.

A comprehensive review of current building services design practice and calculation procedures was carried out in consultation with the industry. This was closely linked to current industry design guides and reference material in order to develop this good practice guidance for building services calculation procedures, including:

- An overview of the building services design process;
- Flowcharts of key calculation sequences;
- Practical procedures and calculation sheets covering 30 key building services calculation design topics;
- Clear cross-referencing to the CIBSE Guide and other appropriate reference sources.

The calculation sheets provide an overview of each procedure, with guidance on design information, inputs and outputs, design tips and watchpoints and worked examples, to aid the design process and reduce errors. They are supplemented with illustrations and guidance on how to use appropriate tables, figures and design information correctly.

Intended users
This guidance is intended for practising building services design engineers, and will be particularly relevant to junior engineers and students on building services courses. Junior engineers would be expected to use it under supervision, (for example within a formal company training scheme) as part of their practical design work. Students can use it within the taught framework or industrial training component of their course, guided by course tutors as appropriate. The guidance should also encourage clear recording and referencing of calculation procedures which will aid quality assurance requirements and allow simpler and easier in-house checking of design work.

The guidance complements the CIBSE Guides, in particular Guide A covering design data, Guide B1 covering heating, Guide B2 covering ventilation and air conditioning, Guide B3 covering ductwork, and Guide C covering reference data. It especially complements the CIBSE Concise Guide[8] a companion volume showing the use and practical application of commonly used design data from other CIBSE Guides.

The Practical Guide to Building Services calculations also closely complements the BSRIA Guide: Design Checks for HVAC – a quality control framework for building services engineers[3]. This provides good practice guidance for building services technical procedures and design management, including design guidance sheets for 60 key design topics and check sheets that can be used in project quality assurance procedures.

New entrants to building services may find it helpful to read the overview information given in the BSRIA illustrated guides volumes 1 and 2.[9]

THE BUILDING SERVICES DESIGN PROCESS

Calculation procedures are a necessary component of design but it is important to see them in the context of the whole design process. Decisions made as part of initial design and during the calculation procedures will affect system design, installation, operation and control.

The BSRIA publication *Design Checks for HVAC – a quality control framework for building services engineers*[3], provides a useful and relevant discussion of the building services design process. As part of this work, a detailed analysis of design procedures and tasks was carried out for building services design and a simple linear model of the building services design process derived was derived as shown. This gives a single design sequence, from statement of need, through problem analysis, synthesis and evaluation to final solution and enables design tasks to be clearly linked to both preceding and succeeding actions. Some primary feedback loops are shown, but in practice there are often feedback loops between all tasks and even within specific tasks.

This work also mapped the building services design process, both as a sequence of design tasks and as a series of topics that make up the design process. This detailed map of the process is shown opposite. The map is shown as a linear view of design, (with iteration and intermediate feedback omitted) in the form of an Ishikawa or fishbone diagram. The process originates from the client's need on the left with various branches feeding into the main design line to eventually reach design completion and design feedback. The map may be of particular benefit to junior engineers as it will enable them to put their contribution to the whole design process in context. When engineers carry out load calculations or pipe sizing, it is easy to forget that this is part of a larger process with consequences for impact on future system installation, operation and control.

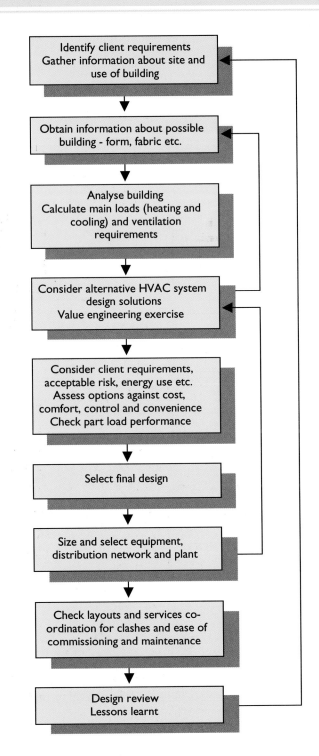

© BSRIA BG 30/2003

THE BUILDING SERVICES DESIGN PROCESS

HVAC Design "Map"

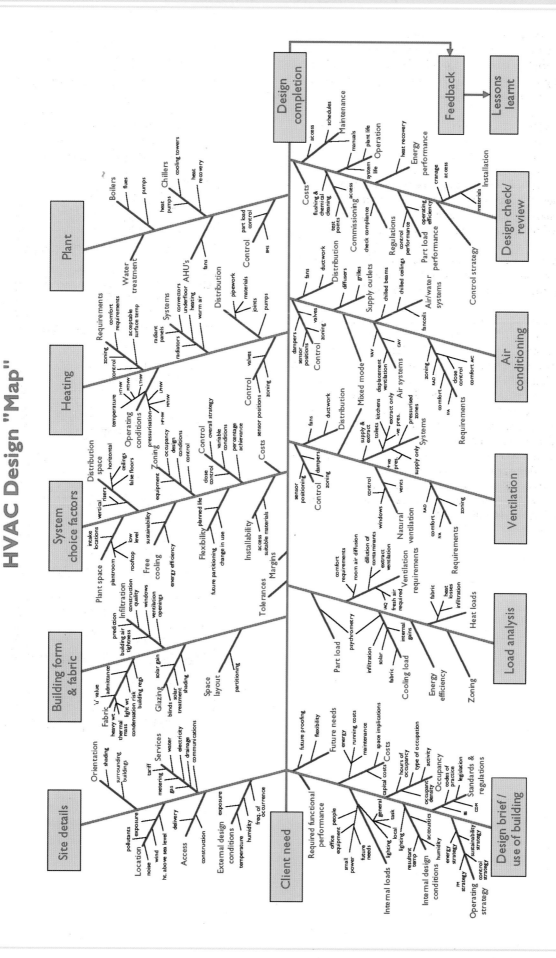

© BSRIA BG 30/2003

OVERVIEW OF CALCULATION SHEETS

The calculation sheets are organised into four sections covering some 30 topics relevant to building services design:

Heating loads and plant
This section covers the key topics and calculations relevant to establishing heat loads for a space or building and sizing heating plant, covering infiltration, U values, heat loss, heating load, radiator sizing and boiler sizing. It explains how to use design data from different sources to establish heat losses and heating loads and explains the different components that make up plant loads.

Cooling loads and plant
This section covers the key topics and calculations relevant to establishing cooling loads for a space or building and sizing cooling plant, covering internal gains, external gains, cooling load, supply air temperature, cooler battery sizing and humidifier duty selection. It provides an overview of heat gains, explains maximum simultaneous loads and explains how to determine acceptable supply air temperatures and size plant components.

Water flow distribution systems
This section covers the key topics and calculations relevant to the sizing of water flow distribution systems, covering pipe sizing, system resistance, pump sizing and water system pressurisation. It explains how to read information from pipe sizing tables, how to work out pressure loss through pipe fittings, and how to determine the index run.

Air flow distribution systems
This section covers the key topics and calculations relevant to the sizing of air flow distribution systems, covering duct sizing, system resistance, fan sizing, grille and diffuser sizing, and space pressurisation. It explains how to read information from the CIBSE duct sizing chart, how to convert from circular to rectangular duct sizes, discusses practical selection of duct sizes to enable economic system installation, explains how to work out pressure loss through duct fittings, and how to apply corrections for air density changes.

Calculation flowcharts are provided at the beginning of each section as shown opposite. These show the calculation procedures in that section and help to explain how different calculation routines link in sequence to build up the design process. This enables any one calculation sequence to be viewed in the context of the broader design process. Some other relevant design inputs and related processes are also shown for completeness, although they are not included in this current guidance as detailed calculation procedures.

Although the calculation procedures provided in this guide are grouped into four sections with calculation sequence flowcharts given for each section, during a real design process all the sections will inter-link. For example, emitter and boiler sizing will require consideration of pipe sizing, boiler sizing needs, details of heater batteries, duct sizing requires consideration of heating and cooling loads and ventilation requirements.

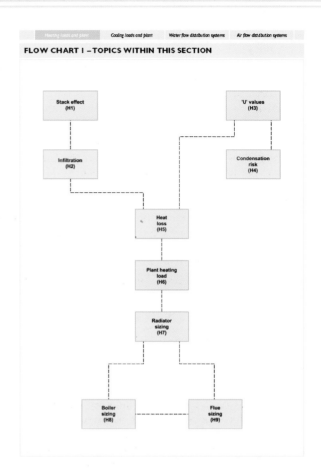

For each calculation topic the guidance provides the following information, as appropriate:

Overview
An overview of the calculation topic and procedure explaining what it is and where and when it is used to put it in context.

Design information required
This explains literally what you need to know to carry out a particular calculation, such as the design information necessary for a procedure, for related design decisions, system layouts or selection of equipment. This could include design data such as an internal design temperature or a mass flow rate, fluid type and temperature, and other design information such as duct material, insulation details and floor to ceiling heights.

Key design inputs
Key technical data (with units) essential for that particular calculation procedure such as mass flow rate, heating load, and limiting pressure drops.

Design outputs
The required design output from a particular calculation procedure which will be used to either inform future design, or to form part of the specification or design production, such as schedules of loads, schematic diagrams, system layout drawings with sizes and design data included, and schedules of equipment sizes and duties.

OVERVIEW OF CALCULATION SHEETS

Design approach
This provides guidance on the design approach to be considered during a calculation procedure and points to be aware of such as designing to minimise noise, the need to check that all of a system is under positive static pressure and the need to reduce corrosion risk.

Calculation procedure
This provides step-by-step procedural guidance, explaining the use of any charts or tables that are likely to be used.

Note: While the calculation procedures are as comprehensive as possible, no design guidance manual can be fully comprehensive for all design applications. It is the responsibility of the designer to add additional information as required by a particular project. Every design project is different and has differing needs and it is the responsibility of the design engineer to fully consider all design requirements

Example
One or more worked examples to illustrate the calculation procedure in detail.

Rule of thumb design data/ cross-check data
Relevant rule-of-thumb data which could be used (with caution) to provide reasonable data for use in design, such as selection of an acceptable pressure drop for use in pipe or duct sizing, or could be used to provide an approximate order of magnitude, a cross-check on a design output such as a watts per square metre, or watts per cubic metre check on a heating load.

References
Reference to relevant design information sources, such as *CIBSE Guides*, BSRIA publications, and *Building Regulations*.

See also:
Reference to other relevant calculation sheets in this guide.

Design tips
These provide practical design tips at the point where they are relevant during the explanation of the calculation procedure.

> **Design tip:** For example, the tips could include checking ceiling space available for ductwork distribution, checking both velocity and pressure drops are acceptable.

Design watchpoints
These provide guidance on things to watch out for or be aware of during the design process. An example is shown below.

DESIGN WATCHPOINTS

. For example, the design watchpoints could include checking that the minimum fresh air requirement is always met, to cross-check computer outputs, to check noise levels are acceptable from selected grilles and diffusers, to ensure that duct dimensions selected are standard or readily available sizes.

Use of the guidance
Design calculations are part of the design process and therefore will form part of the project design file and records and be subject to standard in-company quality assurance (QA) and quality control (QC) procedures. As such they should always be properly recorded and checked. By clearly identifying required design inputs and design outputs in this guidance, and providing a clear methodology, users are encouraged to follow a good practice approach to design. Junior engineers would be expected to use this guidance within a framework of adequate supervision within their organisations, however the following notes highlight some good practice approaches to the use of design calculations.

Identify data sources
It is good practice to clearly record/cross-reference to data sources to enable input information to be adequately verified and to allow track-back of data if necessary. This is particularly important if changes occur in the design which necessitate reworking certain design calculations. Data used should be clearly identified as eg from a client brief (with date and design file reference), or from good practice sources such as the CIBSE Guides, BSRIA publications, British Standards etc. (again with precise details of the publication, date and exact source reference eg page number, table etc),

State assumptions
Where any assumptions are made in the calculation process because data is currently unknown these should be made overt, ie clearly noted as assumptions, and if necessary approved by a senior engineer. Assumptions made should always be reviewed at the end of any calculation process to check again that they were reasonable. If a calculation will need to be redone when more detailed information is provided (eg from a client, manufacturer etc) then this should be clearly noted.

Record calculations clearly
Design calculations should always be properly recorded and checked. Always ensure that all calculations are recorded in sufficient detail that they can be clearly followed by others. Be aware that if a problem arises on a project this could mean revisiting calculations several years after they were originally done.

Avoid margins without justification
Margins should never be added during a calculation process without an adequate reason for doing so and with the approval of a senior engineer. Excessive margins can result in system oversizing and poor operational performance and control. If any margins are used they should be clearly identified and a justification given for their use, which should be recorded in the design file. The use of margins should be reviewed at several stages during the design process to check their appropriateness and avoid any duplication or excess eg at the end of a calculation procedure, at design review stage etc.
(For more information on the use of margins in engineering design refer to *Design Checks for HVAC – A Quality Control Framework for Building Services Engineers*[3], topic sheet number 1 – Design Margins and CIBSE Research Report RR04, *Engineering Design Margins*[1].)

OVERVIEW OF CALCULATION TOPICS

Heating loads and plant

H1   Stack effect
H2   Infiltration
H3   U values
H4   Condensation risk
H5   Heat loss
H6   Plant heating load
H7   Radiator sizing
H8   Boiler sizing
H9   Flue sizing

Cooling loads and plant

C1   Internal heat gains
C2   External gains
C3   Cooling plant loads
C4   Ventilation – Fresh air requirements
C5   Supply air quantity and condition
C6   Heating/cooling coil sizing
C7   Humidifier duty

Water flow distribution systems

W1   Pipe sizing – General
W2   Pipe sizing – Straight lengths
W3   Pipe sizing – Pressure drop across fittings
W4   System resistance for pipework – Index run
W5   Pump sizing
W6   Water system pressurisation

Air flow distribution systems

A1   Duct sizing – General
A2   Duct sizing – Selecting a circular duct size
A3   Duct sizing – Circular to rectangular ducts
A4   Duct sizing – Pressure loss through fittings
A5   Duct system – Index run
A6   Fan sizing
A7   Grille and diffuser sizing
A8   Air density correction
A9   Pressurisation of spaces

© BSRIA BG 30/2003

REFERENCES

1   Lawrence Race G, BSRIA, Parand F, BRE, *Engineering Design Margins*, CIBSE Research Report RR04 1997. Available free to CIBSE members at www.cibse.org.

2   Lawrence Race G, Pearson C & De Saulles T, *Feedback for Better Building Services Design*, AG 21/98, BSRIA 1998 ISBN 0 86022 520 8

3   Lawrence Race G, *Design Checks for HVAC – A Quality Control Framework for Building Services Engineers*, AG 1/2002. BSRIA 2002, ISBN 0 86022 589 5

4   From information gathered for the publication *Design Checks for HVAC – A Quality Control Framework for Building Services Engineers*, BSRIA AG 1/2002

5   CIBSE Design Guides, including Volumes: A *Environmental Design*, 1999, ISBN 0 900 953 969; B *Systems & Equipment* 1986/2001, ISBN 1 903287 20 0, ISBN 1 903287 16 2; C *Reference Data 2000,* ISBN 7506 5360 4

6   H Connor, S Dench, P Bates, *An Assessment of Skill Needs in Engineering*. DfEE Skills Dialogues SD2, February 2001.

7   Professor D Gann & Dr A Salter, *Interdisciplinary Skills for the Built Environment Professional*, Arup Foundation 1999.

8   CIBSE, *Concise Guide*, 2001, ISBN 1 903287 17 0

9   De Saulles, T, *Illustrated Guide to Building Services,* 27/99, BSRIA 1999, ISBN 0 86022 543 3, and *Illustrated Guide to Electrical Building Services* AG 14/2001, BSRIA 2001, ISBN 0 86022 586 0

The following section contains nine building services engineering topic areas related to the design of heating systems, including heating loads and plant sizing.

The following two pages contain flow charts of the relevant design and calculation processes.

The first flow chart shows the nine topics within this section.

The second flow chart provides an overview of the process, showing some of the many related topics that need to be considered in the design of heating systems. The boxes highlighted in blue show an area that is fully or partially covered within one of the nine topic areas in this section, or in the rest of the guidance, with the appropriate reference numbers given.

FLOW CHART 1 – TOPICS WITHIN THIS SECTION

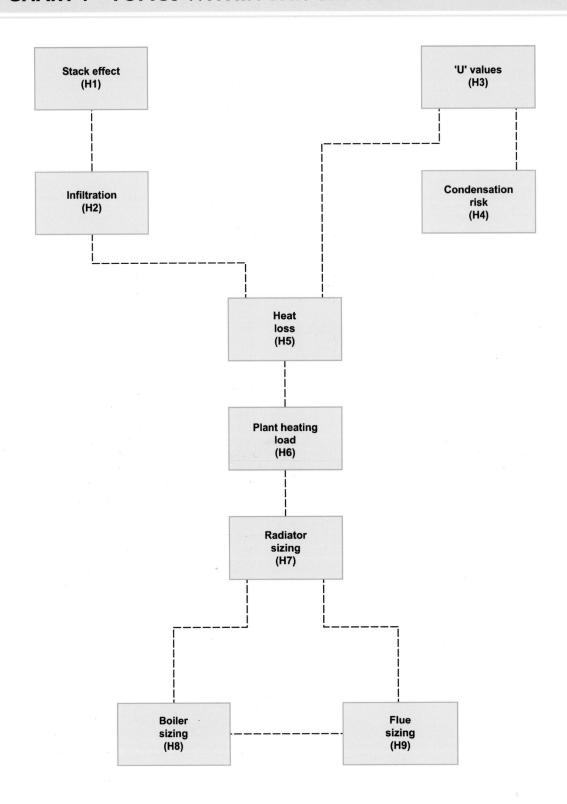

FLOW CHART 2 – OVERVIEW OF SYSTEM DESIGN PROCESS

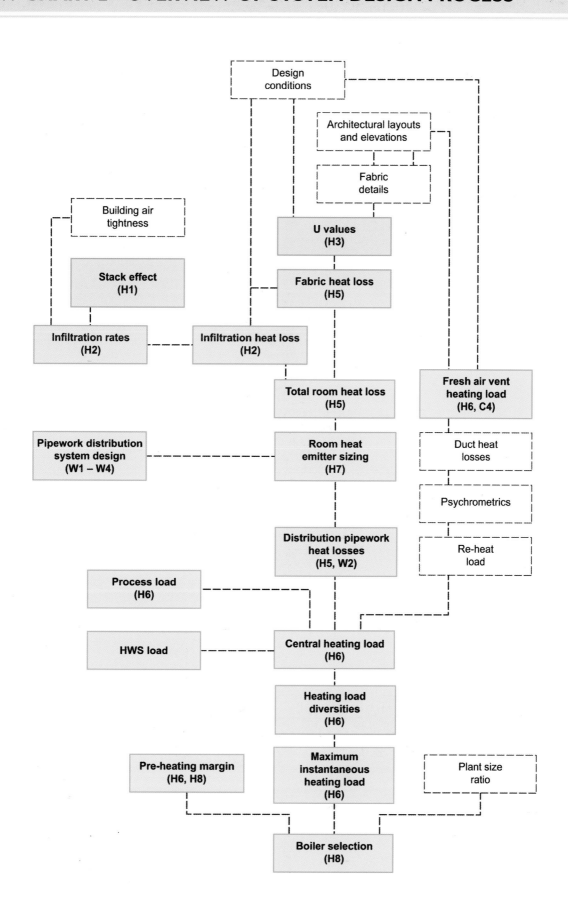

This chart shows the design areas relevant to this design process. Where design areas are wholly or partially discussed in this document the relevant sheet references are given in brackets

H1 STACK EFFECT

Overview

Non-mechanical airflow through a building can occur due to both wind pressure imposed on a building and temperature differences between the inside and outside air.

Stack effect is a difference in pressure caused by a difference between inside and outside air temperature which gives different air densities, thereby causing vertical air movement.

In practice, wind pressures will modify stack effect (this aspect is not dealt with in this sheet). Further information is found in CIBSE AM 10 *Natural ventilation in non-domestic buildings*.

This pressure difference can be used to promote air movement, but will always be dependant on the difference in temperatures, and so may not be practicable for all ventilation applications.

To promote air movement through stack effect, there must be an air inlet point and an air outlet point, and the greater the vertical distance between the two the greater the stack effect.

The direction of air flow will depend on the temperature values. In other words, when the inside temperature is greater than the outside temperature, the resulting air flow will be upwards with air entering through the lower opening and exiting through the higher opening. If, however, the internal temperature should be lower than that outside, then the airflow would reverse, with air entering through the higher opening and leaving through the lower one.

The principle of stack effect can be used for daytime ventilation and also free cooling overnight. This is done by drawing cooler night time air through the building to reduce the internal temperature before occupancy the following morning. This can be very effective at liberating (after occupancy hours) the heat energy stored in the thermal mass of the building structure.

Another use is to limit internal temperature rise within a machine enclosure. Where internal gains are very high, a tall enclosure is constructed with vents or openings at high and low level. The airflow created by the stack effect reduces the internal temperatures to acceptable operating conditions for the machinery.

Standard calculations are available in chapter 4 of *CIBSE Guide A* for the estimation of airflow through simple building layouts. Additional information on wind pressure can also be found in chapter 4. For buildings that have a more complex arrangement of opening layouts, additional information can be found in the CIBSE publication *AM10 Natural ventilation in non-domestic buildings 1997*.

Design information required

Type, size and location of openings

The type and shape of the openings will have an effect on the airflow through them, and so needs to be accurately identified.

Key design inputs

- Inside and outside air temperatures (^{0}C). The difference between inside and outside temperatures affects the difference in density and difference in pressure. The temperature difference is required as it causes the difference in pressure of the internal and external air masses which results in stack effect
- Height difference between inlet and outlet points (m). The greater the difference between the two openings, the greater the stack effect that can be achieved

Design outputs

- Ventilation strategy and specification including ventilation type, such as cross ventilation, single-sided ventilation; schedule of window types, actuators, method of control; and schedule of transfer grilles
- Analysis of predicted ventilation performance
- Requirements for solar shading, where appropriate
- Layout plan drawings showing air flow paths
- Control philosophy to be applied, where appropriate

Calculation approach

1. Select appropriate calculation according to the building layout
2. Identify the inside and outside air temperatures that are to be applied to the calculation
3. Identify the height difference between the inlet and outlet points (centre to centre)
4. Identify the type, size and shape of the opening, (some factors in the equation may vary according to this)
5. Enter values into equation to calculate the volume flow rate through the building.

Example

Calculate the rate of natural airflow due to temperature through the building described below.

Design data

The building has four openings for ventilation, two on each of the opposite sides, one at high level one at low level.

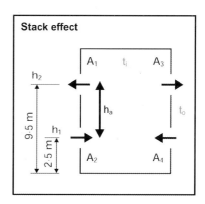

H1 STACK EFFECT

Where:

t_i = Mean inside temperature (^{0}C)
t_o= Mean outside temperature (^{0}C)
A_1, A_2, A_3, A_4 = Opening areas (m^2)
h_1, h_2 = heights above ground of centres of openings (m)
h_a = Difference between heights h_1 and h_2
(9·5 m − 2·5 m = 7 m)

Using equation:

$$Q_b = C_d \times A_b \times \left(\frac{2 \times \Delta t \times h_a\, g}{\overline{t}+273} \right)^{0.5}$$

Where:

Q_b = volumetric flow-rate due to stack effect only (m^3/s)
C_d = discharge coefficient (value for a sharp opening is 0·61)
A_b = equivalent area for ventilation by stack effect only (m)
g = acceleration due to gravity (9·81 m/s^2)
$\overline{t}$ = mean of t_i and t_o (^{0}C)
Δt = temperature difference between inside and outside
A_b = found from:

$$\frac{1}{A_b^{\,2}} = \frac{1}{\left(A_1+A_3\right)^2} + \frac{1}{\left(A_2+A_4\right)^2}$$

Area of openings:

$A_1 = 1$ m^2
$A_2 = 0·75$ m^2
$A_3 = 1$ m^2
$A_4 = 0·75$ m^2

Temperatures:
Summer
t_i = 22^{0}C
t_o = 26^{0}C

Therefore:
Δt = 26-22 = 4^{0}C
$\overline{t}$ = (22 + 26)/2 = 24^{0}C

Find A_b

$$\frac{1}{A_b^{\,2}} = \frac{1}{(1+1)^2} + \frac{1}{(0·75+0·75)^2}$$

$$\frac{1}{A_b^{\,2}} = \frac{1}{2^2} + \frac{1}{1·5^2}$$

$$\frac{1}{A_b^{\,2}} = \frac{1}{4} + \frac{1}{2·25}$$

$$\frac{1}{A_b^{\,2}} = 0·25+0·444 = 0·694$$

$$\frac{1}{0·694} = A_b^{\,2}$$

$$1·44 = A_b^{\,2}$$

Therefore:
$$A_b = \sqrt{1·44} = 1·20\, m^2$$

With all the variables found the flow rate can be calculated:

$$Q_b = 0·61 \times 1·2 \times \left(\frac{2 \times 4 \times 7 \times 9·81}{24+273} \right)^{0.5}$$

$$Q_b = 0·732 \times \left(\frac{549·36}{297} \right)^{0.5}$$

$$Q_b = 0·732 \times (1·849)^{0.5}$$

Therefore:
$$Q_b = 0·732 \times 1·36 = 0·995\ m^3/s$$

References
CIBSE Guide A, *Environmental Design*, 1999, ISBN 0 900 953 969
CIBSE, *Natural Ventilation in Non-Domestic Buildings*, AM10, 1997, ISBN 0 900953 55 1
AIVC 1998, *TN 44 Numerical Data for Air Infiltration & Natural Ventilation Calculations*, ISBN 1946075972

See also:
Sheet H2 Infiltration
Sheet H5 Heat loss
Sheet C1 Internal heat gains
Sheet C2 External gains
Sheet C4 Ventilation − Fresh air requirements
Sheet A8 Air density correction
Sheet A9 Pressurisation of spaces

DESIGN WATCHPOINTS

1. Be sure of the direction of airflow as it may change through the year as the outside temperature changes.
2. Make sure that airflow induced by stack effect does not cause problems with over-pressurising a space, or disturbing the design airflow patterns of ventilation and air conditioning systems.
3. Wind pressures acting on the building may nullify the pressure difference induced by stack effect.
4. Air paths or openings, provided to make use of airflow from the stack effect, might affect heat loss if they are not able to be closed.
5. Openings for stack effect airflow may represent a security risk if they are not satisfactorily secured.
6. Internal partitions and obstructions may lessen the effect by imposing greater resistance on the flow of air. Stack effect should ideally be limited to single zone areas.

H2 INFILTRATION

Overview

Infiltration can be outside air, which enters a building or room, or internal air at a different temperature that enters a room. Air enters the building through defects or imperfections in the external façade, such as small gaps, and through cracks around windows and doors. This is due to an air pressure difference caused by wind pressure or temperature differences.

Infiltration should not be confused with a mechanical air change rate or with natural ventilation, which is the deliberate provision of outside fresh air for ventilation by non-mechanical means.

In winter it can cause additional heat loss as air enters the space at outdoor conditions, and in summer it can cause additional heat gain. Therefore, the volume of infiltration air must be considered as part of the heating and cooling load calculation.

Pressurising a building will reduce infiltration but will incur costs in terms of both energy and plant.

Air tightness testing

With effect from 1 October 2003, it is recommended that in order to comply with *Building Regulations Approved Document Part L2*, any new building must be designed and built to have a maximum air permeability of $10 \ m^3/(h.m^2)$. This typically equates to an air leakage index of $15 m^3/(h.m^2)$. The recommended air leakage standards in Table 1, Section 5 of *CIBSE TM23,* and BSRIA TN 19/01 *Air Tightness Testing,* can be significantly lower than this depending on the type of building and whether good or best practice is applied. These values can be achieved with a robust building design combined with good construction techniques and careful site supervision.

For work on existing buildings, air tightness testing is not required. Section 4 of the *Building Regulations Approved Document Part L2*, 2002 gives guidance on improving air tightness.

One method of demonstrating compliance with the *Building Regulations* for new buildings is to carry out air leakage tests in accordance with *CIBSE TM23*. The CIBSE and BSRIA recommended standards are for different types of buildings, for good practice and best practice and are given in terms of air leakage index and air permeability. These values are substantially lower than those permitted under the *Building Regulations.*

If the building has less than $1000 \ m^2$ gross floor area an alternate method to air tightness testing to show compliance is to provide certificates or declarations of appropriate design details and building techniques, see section 2.2 of *The Building Regulations Approved Document Part L2*, 2002.

It is expected that the requirement for testing will result in realised infiltration rates falling.

Air leakage index and air permeability

Air leakage index and air permeability have the same units of $m^3/(h.m^2)$.

Air leakage index Q_{50}/S, is the air leakage rate at a pressure difference of 50 Pa divided by the building envelope area S. S does not include the lower floor area unless the floor is not supported by the ground.

Air permeability Q_{50}/S_T, is the air leakage rate at a pressure difference of 50 Pa divided by the building envelope area S_T. S_T includes the ground floor area for all types of building.

The *Building Regulations Approved Document Part L2* gives required performance levels in terms of air permeability but, as already discussed, recommended standards for both terms are available in *CIBSE TM23* and *BSRIA TN 19/01.*

Infiltration heat loss calculation using air leakage index

The following is only one method of calculating the heat loss due to infiltration, and it is suggested that advice is sought from a senior engineer as to an organisation's preferred calculation methodology and assumptions.

Section 6 of *CIBSE TM23* gives a calculation that allows the infiltration rate in ach^{-1} to be determined from the air leakage index. The actual air leakage index will not be known until the building is tested, but maximum compliance levels are in force. It is reasonable to determine a maximum infiltration rate for average wind conditions for design purposes.

Design information required

Building details and dimensions

These can be obtained from the architect's detailed drawings. This should include the height as well as the plan dimensions, whether the lower floor is supported by solid ground or if there is a basement or car park under the building.

Internal surface area S (m^2)

The internal surface area of the building façade is required. For the air leakage index, S does not include the ground or lowest floor area unless special circumstances apply. (See *CIBSE TM 23* section 3.3.1)

Volume V (m^3)

The internal volume of the building being tested

Air leakage index Q_{50}/S ($m^3/(h.m^2)$)

The recommended air leakage index for the type of building needs to be known. Values can be found in Table 1, Section 5 of *CIBSE TM23,* for good practice and best practice.

H2 INFILTRATION

Q_{50} (m³/h)

Q_{50} is determined from air tightness testing. It is the rate at which air leaks from a building when pressurised to 50 Pa. From this, value, Q_{50}, the air leakage index of a building can be determined by dividing Q_{50} by S.

For example:

Air leakage index = Q_{50}/S

Therefore:

Q_{50} = air leakage index x S

Δt (K)

The difference between the external and internal temperature.

Key design inputs

- Internal surface area S (m²), excluding ground floor
- Volume V (m³)
- Air leakage index (Q_{50}/S)
- Leakage airflow rate at 50 Pa Q_{50} (m³/h)
- Δt air temperature (K)

Design outputs

- I is the infiltration rate in air changes per hour for design purposes. It should be noted that some texts use N to denote air change rates in ventilation calculations; take care not to confuse the two
- Qv is the infiltration heat loss (kW)

Calculation procedure

Step 1. The key design inputs are established and applied to the following equation (equation from Section 6 *CIBSE TM23*):

$$I = \frac{1}{20} \times \frac{S}{V} \times \frac{Q_{50}}{S}$$

giving an average infiltration rate in air changes per hour for average weather conditions.

The equation is formed in three parts:

$\dfrac{Q_{50}}{S}$ is the air leakage index,

$\dfrac{1}{20}$ is applied to the air leakage index to approximate the air infiltration rate in air changes per hour for dwellings,

$\dfrac{S}{V}$ the surface to volume ratio, is then applied to approximate air infiltration rate in air changes per hour for non-domestic buildings.

Step 2. Apply the value for infiltration to the heat loss calculation:

$$Q_v = \frac{1}{3} \times I \times V \times \Delta T$$

Example

Calculate the design heat loss due to infiltration for a three-storey office building with balanced mechanical ventilation from the following data:

Maximum air leakage index for good practice = 5·0 (m³/h)/m²
Internal dimensions: 15 m wide, 30 m long, 9 m high.
Temperatures: 21°C internal, –3°C external.

Step 1. Establish:
Internal surface area S (m²), excluding ground floor,
Volume V (m³)
Q_{50} (m³/h)

$$S = \{2 \times (30 + 15) \times 9\} + (30 \times 15) = 1260 \text{ m}^2$$

$$V = 30 \times 15 \times 9 = 4050 \text{ m}^3$$

air leakage index = 5 = Q_{50}/S

Apply to infiltration equation:

$$I = \frac{1}{20} \times \frac{1260}{4050} \times 5$$
$$I = 0 \cdot 077 \text{ ach}^{-1}$$

Step 2. Apply to ventilation heat loss calculation:

$$Q_v = \frac{1}{3} \times 0 \cdot 077 \times 4050 \times 24$$
$$Q_v = 2520 \text{ W ie } 2 \cdot 52 \text{kW}$$

H2 INFILTRATION

References

CIBSE TM23, *Testing Buildings for Air Leakage*, 2000, ISBN 1903287103

See also:

Sheet H5 Heat loss
Sheet H6 Plant heating load
Sheet H8 Boiler sizing
Sheet C3 Cooling plant load
Sheet C4 Ventilation – Fresh air requirements
Sheet A9 Pressurisation of spaces

Lawrence Race G, *Design Checks for HVAC – A Quality Control Framework for Building Services Engineers* – sheet 19, AG 1/2002, BSRIA 2002, ISBN 0 86022 589 5
Building Regulations Approved Document Part F – Ventilation: 1995 Edition, amended 2000, ISBN 0 11752 932 X
Building Regulations Approved Document Part L2 – Conservation of fuel and power: 2002 Edition, ISBN 0 11753 610 5
Potter I N, *Air Tightness Testing – A Guide for Clients and Contractors*, TN 19/2001, BSRIA 2001, ISBN 0 86022 592 5
Potter I N, *Air Tightness Specification for Quality Buildings*, TN 10/98, BSRIA 1998, ISBN 0 86022 499 6
Potter I N, Jones T J, Booth W B, *Air Leakage of Office Buildings*, TN 8/95, BSRIA 1995, ISBN 0 86022 402 3
CIBSE Guide A, *Environmental Design*, Section 4, *1999*, ISBN 0 900 953 969
CIBSE, *Natural Ventilation Non-Domestic Buildings*, AM10, CIBSE 1997, ISBN 0 900953 55 1

DESIGN WATCHPOINTS

1. It must be borne in mind that an airtightness index of 5 $m^3/(h.m^2)$ is only achieved by the combination of good design details, good construction techniques and careful site supervision.
2. Use dimensions given on the drawings wherever possible rather than scaling off. Drawings can distort during the copying process, resulting in inaccuracies when measuring from the print.
3. Air infiltration through the building fabric should be minimised by installing air barriers. Certificates or declarations should be provided or obtained by the person carrying out the work. Designers should refer to the *Building Regulations Approved Document Part L2* for more information.
4. The values for air leakage index given in *CIBSE TM23* are substantially lower than those permitted by the *Building Regulations*, being applicable to good and best practice.
5. Not all four sides of a building will be subjected to infiltration at the same time. How much and where will depend on the weather conditions at the time and the location/orientation of the building. Check with senior engineers as there may be a set company procedure, such as only considering 50% of the calculated infiltration rate at any one time.
6. Note that the equation in *CIBSE TM23* relates the seasonal average infiltration rate to airtightness. While this is useful for energy calculations, for design sizing purposes, it may be underestimating the infiltration load that occurs at the design extremes.
7. While point five above is valid, in practice the diversity is not often taken into account; this will offset to an extent, the underestimating referred to in point six for system and boiler sizing. Do remember that, for room heat emitter sizing, the full local infiltration rate must be considered. Care should also be taken as the infiltration part of the calculation assumes greater importance with increasing levels of insulation.

H3 U VALUES

Overview

The U value is the common term for unit thermal transmittance, and is used in the calculation of heat losses and gains. The thermal transmittance is a result of the relationship between the thermal resistances of a particular element or elements, and can be determined through calculation. The calculation of U values for composite walls, roofs and floors can be very complex. The *Building Regulations Approved Document Part L2* lists at least 21 standards and guides for calculation methods and devotes approximately one third of its 75 pages to tables and examples related to U values. This guidance sheet is a very simplified overview. Additional examples are also available in *Building Regulations Approved Document Part L2* for different wall constructions and for floors and glazing.

Software for calculating U Values is available such as the U Value Calculator, by BRE. When using any kind of software package, whether it is for U values or other building services calculations, check that it reflects the current regulations in place at the time.

The thermal resistance, R, of a structural element can be calculated from:

$$R = \frac{d}{\lambda}$$

Where:
d = thickness of element (m)
λ = thermal conductivity (W/mK)
The basic formula for calculating the U value of an element or structure is:

$$U = \frac{1}{R_T}$$

Where: $R_T = \frac{R_{Upper} + R_{Lower}}{2}$

Therefore: $U = \frac{2}{R_L + R_U}$

Where:
R_U = upper bound thermal resistance (m²K/W)
R_L = lower bound thermal resistance (m²K/W)
R_T = thermal resistance of section (m²K/W)
U = thermal transmittance (W/m²K)
R_{si} = inside surface resistance (m²K/W)
R_{se} = outside surface resistance (m²K/W)
R_a = resistance of air space (m²K/W)

Design information required

Construction
The detailed build-up of the wall or roof that is being considered, including dimensions.

Materials
The exact type of materials being used (for example lightweight or heavyweight blockwork; this can have a significant effect on the U value obtained), and the thermal conductivity (or thermal resistance) of each material. Wherever possible, the actual manufacturer's details should be used, as there may be a difference between the values of thermal conductivity, for instance, of an item from one manufacturer to another. Values of thermal conductivity can be found in *CIBSE Guide A*, Appendix 3.

R_{si} will depend upon direction of heat flow (horizontal/up/down)

R_{se} will depend upon direction of heat flow and wind speed. Appendix A of *the Building Regulations Approved Document Part L2* edition has tables of U values for different materials and construction and example calculations.

Calculation procedure

Bridged walls
This is the combined method of calculating U values in terms of proportions of the total surface area.

Step 1. For each bridged layer, calculate the proportion (P) of the surface area that is each material.

Step 2. Find the thermal resistance of each material (if not already known):

$$R = \frac{d}{\lambda}$$

Where:
R = Thermal resistance (m²K/W)
d = Thickness of material (m)
λ = Thermal conductivity (W/mK)

Step 3. If possible, split the wall into sections, from an external or internal surface to a cavity, or from cavity to cavity. The thermal resistance for each section that contains no bridging (each layer consists of only one material) can then be calculated by simply summing the thermal resistances for each layer in that section (including surface resistances). For bridged sections (one or more layers have two or more component materials), a thermal resistance must be calculated for each possible route through the section by summing the thermal resistances of the component parts (if a wall has two layers, each with two materials a and b and c and d respectively), there are four routes: a–c, b–c, a–d, b–d. The thermal resistance for each route would be: $R_{(a-c)} = (R_a + R_c)$. Each route will also have an associated proportion, which is found using: $P_{(a-c)} = P_a \times P_c$.

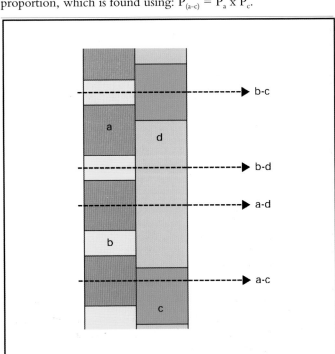

H3 U VALUES

The thermal resistance for the entire section can then be found as follows:

$$\frac{1}{R_T} = \frac{P_{(a-c)}}{R_{(a-c)}} + \frac{P_{(a-d)}}{R_{(a-d)}} + \frac{P_{(b-c)}}{R_{(b-c)}} + \frac{P_{(b-d)}}{R_{(b-d)}}$$

Where:

R_T = thermal resistance of section (m²K/W)

Step 4. The upper bound of the thermal resistance can then be found by simply summing the thermal resistances of all the individual sections.

Step 5. The lower bound is the sum of the thermal resistances of each layer. For a bridged layer, this is the sum of (P x R) for each material in that layer.

Step 6. The U value can then be calculated as follows:

$$U = \frac{2}{\left(R_U + R_L\right)}$$

Where:

U = thermal transmittance (W/m²K)

R_U = upper bound thermal resistance (m²K/W)

R_L = lower bound thermal resistance (m²K/W)

Example – Bridged cavity wall

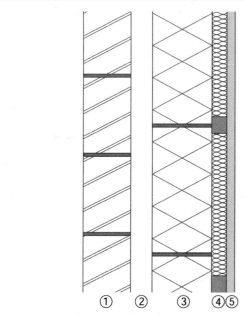

1   0·105 m brickwork

2   0·05 m air cavity

3   0·125 m concrete blocks (0·44 m x 0·215 m) bridged by 0·01 m mortar joints

4   0·03 m insulation betwen timber studs (0·05 m x 0·03 m) at 0·6 m centres

5   0·013 m plasterboard

Note: As the thermal conductivities, of brickwork and mortar differ by approximately 0·1 W/mK, the mortar in the brickwork can be ignored in the calculation.

Thermal conductivities:

Brickwork: λ_b = 0·77 W/mK

Very lightweight areated concrete blocks: λ_c = 0·11 W/mK

Mortar: λ_m = 0·88 W/mK

Insulation: λ_i = 0·04 W/mK

Timber: λ_t = 0·14 W/mK

Plasterboard: λ_p = 0·16 W

Surface resistances:

External surface: R_{se} = 0·06 m²K/W

Internal surface: R_{si} = 0·12 m²K/W

Air cavity: R_a = 0·18 m²K/W

Step 1. Calculate the proportions of each bridged layer (in this case 3 and 4) that are each material.

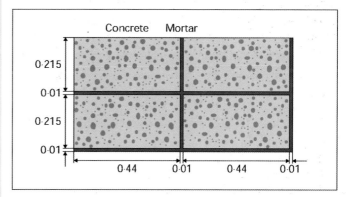

Layer 3:

Area of the concrete is 4 x 0·215 x 0·44 = 0·3784 m²

Total area is 4 x (0·215 + 0·01) x (0·44 + 0·01) = 0·405 m²

Proportion of concrete is 0·3784 ÷ 0·405 = 0·9343

Proportion of mortar is 1 - 0·9343 = 0·0657

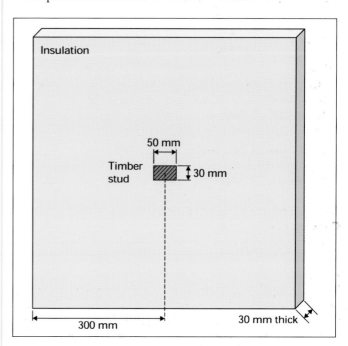

Layer 4:

Area of the wood is 0·03 x 0·05 = 0·0015 m²

Total area is (0·05 + 0·55) x (0·03 + 0·57) = 0·36 m²

Proportion of wood is 0·0015 ÷ 0·36 = 0·00417

Proportion of Insulation is 1 – 0·00417 = 0·9958

© BSRIA BG 30/2003

H3 U VALUES

Step 2. Use the depth and the thermal conductivity of each material to calculate the thermal resistance.

$$R = d \div \lambda$$
$$R_b = 0.105 \div 0.77 = 0.136 \text{ m}^2\text{K/W}$$
$$R_c = 0.125 \div 0.11 = 1.14 \text{ m}^2\text{K/W}$$
$$R_m = 0.125 \div 0.88 = 0.142 \text{ m}^2\text{K/W}$$
$$R_t = 0.03 \div 0.14 = 0.21 \text{ m}^2\text{K/W}$$
$$R_i = 0.03 \div 0.04 = 0.75 \text{ m}^2\text{K/W}$$
$$R_p = 0.013 \div 0.16 = 0.081 \text{ m}^2\text{K/W}$$

Step 3. Calculate the Thermal resistance of each section:

Section I (no bridging)

From External Surface to midpoint of cavity

$$R_I = R_{se} + R_b + \tfrac{1}{2}R_a$$
$$= 0.06 + 0.136 + \tfrac{1}{2} \times 0.18$$
$$= 0.286 \text{ m}^2\text{K/W}$$

Section II (bridged)

Possible routes:

i. cavity – **concrete block – insulation** – plasterboard – internal wall
ii. cavity – **concrete block – timber** – plasterboard – internal wall
iii. cavity – **mortar – insulation** – plasterboard – internal wall
iv. cavity – **mortar – timber** – plasterboard – internal wall

$$R_1 = \frac{1}{2}R_a + R_c + R_i + R_p + R_{si} = 2.18 \text{ m}^2\text{K/W}$$
$$P_1 = P_c \times P_i = 0.930$$

$$R_2 = \frac{1}{2}R_a + R_c + R_t + R_p + R_{si} = 1.64 \text{ m}^2\text{K/W}$$
$$P_2 = P_c \times P_t = 0.00390$$

$$R_3 = \frac{1}{2}R_a + R_m + R_i + R_p + R_{si} = 1.18 \text{ m}^2\text{K/W}$$
$$P_3 = P_m \times P_i = 0.0654$$

$$R_4 = \frac{1}{2}R_a + R_m + R_t + R_p + R_{si} = 0.64 \text{ m}^2\text{K/W}$$
$$P_4 = P_m \times P_t = 0.000274$$

$$\frac{1}{R_{II}} = \frac{P_1}{R_1} + \frac{P_2}{R_2} + \frac{P_3}{R_3} + \frac{P_4}{R_4} = 0.485$$
$$R_{II} = 2.06 \text{ m}^2\text{K/W}$$

Step 4. Use the thermal resistances for each section to calculate the upper bound thermal resistance:

$$R_U = (R_I + R_{II})$$
$$= (0.286 + 2.06)$$
$$= 2.346 \text{ m}^2\text{K/W}$$

Step 5. Calculate the lower bound thermal resistance.

$$R_L = 0.06 + 0.136 + 0.18 + \big((1.14 \times 0.9343) + (0.142 \times 0.0657)\big)$$
$$+ \big((0.21 \times 0.0417) + (0.75 \times 0.9958)\big) + 0.081 + 0.12$$
$$R_L = 2.399 \text{ m}^2\text{K/W}$$

Step 6. Use the upper and lower bound thermal resistances to calculate the U value.

$$U = \frac{2}{(R_U + R_L)}$$
$$= \frac{2}{(2.346 + 2.399)}$$
$$= \frac{2}{4.745}$$
$$= 0.421 \text{ Wm}^2\text{K}$$

Design data

Details on various fabric elements, as well as values for inside, outside and air resistances, can be found from specific manufacturers, or general guidance information is given in *CIBSE Guide A*.

References:

CIBSE Guide A, *Environmental Design,* Section 3, CIBSE 1999, ISBN 0 900 953 969
Building Regulations Approved Document Part L2, 2002, ISBN 0 11753 610 5

See also:

Sheet H2 Infiltration
Sheet H5 Heat loss
Sheet H8 Boiler sizing
Sheet C4 Ventilation – Fresh air requirements

Lawrence Race G, *Design Checks for HVAC – A Quality Control Framework for Building Services Engineers* – sheet 20, AG 1/2002, BSRIA 2002, ISBN 0 86022 589 5

DESIGN WATCHPOINTS

1. All new constructions in the UK must have the building constructed with U values complying with the current edition of *Building Regulations Approved Document Part L2*. This will also involve any impending changes to standards for declaring of conductivity of insulation that accounts for ageing effects.
2. Use the dimensions shown on the drawings wherever possible rather than scaling off, as the drawings may become distorted while being copied.
3. Wherever possible, base the calculations on the data of the actual manufacturer of the materials being used.
4. When calculating U values stop to think about what is being calculated. For example when calculating windows, the glass may have a very low U value but the frame will be higher which will affect the overall U value of the window when considered as a single unit.

H4 CONDENSATION RISK

Overview

Condensation is the precipitation of moisture or water vapour, normally present in the air, when it meets surfaces or materials at a temperature below the dew point of the air.

Properties of humid air are given in various sources such as section 1 of *CIBSE Guide C,* and on the CIBSE psychrometric charts.

There are two types of condensation to be considered:

1. Surface or superficial condensation

Surface condensation is formed when moist air comes in contact with a surface that is below the dewpoint of the air. This is most commonly seen on the inside of single-glazed windows in winter.

2. Interstitial or internal condensation

This is where condensation occurs actually within the building element or fabric itself, rather than on the surface, and is formed when the vapour pressure at any point through the structure equals the saturated vapour pressure corresponding to the temperature at that point. This is undesirable as it can cause deterioration of the building fabric and can lead to mould growth.

Design information required

Construction details

The type and thickness of the individual components that make up the particular element.

Psychrometric tables

These can be found in *CIBSE Guide C,* Section 1.

Key design inputs

- Outside design temperature °C. The value to be used as the lowest outside temperature that can be reached, and the design internal temperatures that can still be achieved. (See *CIBSE Guide A,* section 2.)
- Inside design temperature °C. The required temperature within the room or space. (See *CIBSE Guide A,* section 1.)
- Thermal conductivity W/mK. The thermal conductivity for each material in the wall. Alternatively, the thermal resistance can be used. (See manufacturers data or *CIBSE Guide A* section 3.)
- Vapour resistivity GNs/kgm. The vapour resistivity for each material in the wall must be known. Alternatively, the vapour resistance can be used. (See manufacturers data or *CIBSE Guide A* section 3.)
- Surface resistances (m²K/W) of any cavities and the internal and external surfaces
- Vapour pressure kPa inside and outside

Calculation procedure

Step 1. If not already known, use the values of thermal conductivity (λ), vapour resistivity (r) and thickness (d) to calculate the thermal resistance (R) and vapour resistance (G) for each material:

$$R = d \div \lambda$$
$$G = d \times r$$

Step 2. Number each node (each node is where two different materials meet), and work out the temperature (t) and vapour pressure (P_v) at each node.

Temperature at node $_n$ = inside surface temperature − (inside surface − outside surface temperature) (resistance between inside surface and node/total resistance of structure)

$$t_n = t_{si} - \left(\left((t_{si} - t_{se}) \times \sum_{si}^{n} R \right) \div \sum_{si}^{se} R \right)$$

$$P_{vn} = P_{vsi} - \left(\left((P_{vsi} - P_{vse}) \times \sum_{si}^{n} G \right) \div \sum_{si}^{se} G \right)$$

Where:

$_n$ = node number

$_{si}$ = internal surface

$_{se}$ = external surface

$\sum y$ means sum of y between the node numbered below, and the node numbered above.

Step 3. Use CIBSE tables from *Guide C* section 1 to find saturated vapour pressure (P_s) for each node (use value for 100% saturation for each temperature). As the values are only given for every 0·5°C, you may need to interpolate between temperatures to find the correct value.

Step 4. If $P_v < P_s$ then no condensation will form at that node, but if $P_v \geq P_s$ then there will be condensation (a value of P_v higher than the value of P_s for the same temperature represents a saturation higher than 100%, which is not possible, so the excess moisture condenses). If there is condensation at a node, the calculation method must be repeated to check that condensation will not form elsewhere. This is done by splitting at the nodes with condensation and using the value of P_s as the value for P_v for those nodes (it is impossible for P_v to be higher than P_s, and changing the value of P_v at the node could adversely affect the other nodes).

© BSRIA BG 30/2003

H4 CONDENSATION RISK

Example

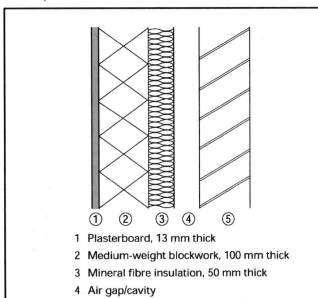

1 Plasterboard, 13 mm thick
2 Medium-weight blockwork, 100 mm thick
3 Mineral fibre insulation, 50 mm thick
4 Air gap/cavity
5 Brickwork, 105 mm thick

Internal conditions: 21°C db
External conditions: -4°C db

➢ **Design tip:** Check the conditions to be used with your senior engineer – see Watchpoints 1 and 2.

Internal vapour pressure: 1·258 kPa
External vapour pressure: 0·437 kPa

Surface resistances:
Internal surface: $R_{si} = 0·12$ m²K/W
External surface: $R_{se} = 0·06$ m²K/W
Air cavity: $R_4 = 0·18$ m²K/W

Thermal conductivities:
Plasterboard: $\lambda_1 = 0·16$ W/mK
Blockwork: $\lambda_2 = 0·51$ W/mK
Insulation: $\lambda_3 = 0·035$ W/mK
Brickwork: $\lambda_5 = 0·84$ W/mK

Vapour resistivities:
Plasterboard: $r_1 = 60$ GNs/kgm
Blockwork: $r_2 = 75$ GNs/kgm
Insulation: $r_3 = 7$ GNs/kgm
Brickwork: $r_5 = 50$ GNs/kgm

Step 1. Calculate the thermal and vapour resistances:

$R_1 = d_1 \div \lambda_1$
$R_1 = 0·013 \div 0·16$
$R_1 = 0·081$ m²K/W

$G_1 = d_1 \times r_1$
$G_1 = 0·013 \times 60$
$G_1 = 0·78$ GNs/kg

The table below shows all the thermal and vapour resistances.

Layer	d (m)	k (W/mK)	r (GNs/kgm)	R (m²K/W)	G (GNs/kg)
Internal surface	-	-	-	0·120	0
Plaster	0·013	0·16	60	0·081	0·78
Blockwork	0·1	0·51	75	0·196	7·5
Mineral insulation	0·05	0·035	7	1·429	0·35
Cavity	-	-	-	0·180	0
Brickwork	0·105	0·84	50	0·125	5·25
External surface	-	-	-	0·060	0

Step 2. The numbers for each node are:

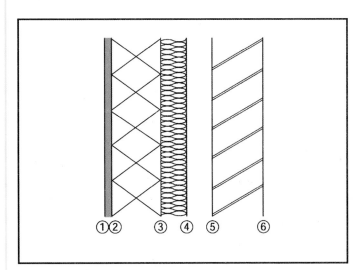

Calculate the temperature and the vapour pressure at each node.

For example for node 3:

$$t_n = t_{si} - \left(\left((t_{si} - t_{se}) \times \sum_{si}^{n} R \right) \div \sum_{si}^{se} R \right)$$

$t_3 = 21 - ((0·120 + 0·081 + 0·196) \div (0·120 + 0·081 + 0·196 + 1·429 + 0·180 + 0·125 + 0·060) \times (21 - -4))$

$t_3 = 21 - (0·397 \div 2·191 \times 25)$

$t_3 = 21 - 4·53$

$t_3 = 16·47°C$

$$P_{vn} = P_{vsi} - \left(\left((P_{vsi} - P_{vse}) \times \sum_{si}^{n} G \right) \div \sum_{si}^{se} G \right)$$

$P_{v3} = 1·258 - ((0 + 0·78 + 7·5) \div (0 + 0·78 + 7·5 + 0·35 + 0 + 5·25 + 0) \times (1·258 - 0·437))$

$P_{v3} = 1·258 - ((8·28 \div 13·88) \times 0·821)$

$P_{v3} = 1·258 - 0·490$

$P_{v3} = 0·768$ kPa

© BSRIA BG 30/2003

H4 CONDENSATION RISK

This table shows the temperatures and vapour pressures for all the nodes.

		t (°C)	P_v (kPa)
Inside	-	21·00	1·2580
Node 1	Inside/plaster	19·63	1·2580
Node 2	Plaster/blockwork	18·70	1·2119
Node 3	Blockwork/insulation	16·47	0·7683
Node 4	Insulation/cavity	0·16	0·7476
Node 5	Cavity/brickwork	-1·89	0·7476
Node 6	Brickwork/outside	-3·32	0·4371
Outside	-	-4·00	0·4371

Step 3. Interpolating between values to find the saturated vapour pressure:

For example Node 4: At 0°C, Ps = 0·6108 kPa; at 0·5 °C, Ps = 0·6333 kPa. Therefore for 0·16°C:

$P_s = 0·6108 + ((0·16-0) ÷ (0·5-0))$ x $(0·6333 − 0·6108)$

$P_s = 0·6108 + 0·0072$

$P_s = 0·618$ kPa

This table shows the saturated vapour pressures.

		t (°C)	P_v (kPa)	P_s (kPa)
Inside	-	21·00	1·2580	2·4860
Node 1	Inside/plaster	19·63	1·2580	2·2846
Node 2	Plaster/blockwork	18·70	1·2119	2·1557
Node 3	Blockwork/insulation	16·47	0·7683	1·8720
Node 4	Insulation/cavity	0·16	0·7476	0·6182
Node 5	Cavity/brickwork	-1·89	0·7476	0·5220
Node 6	Brickwork/outside	-3·32	0·4371	0·4632
Outside	-	-4·00	0·4371	0·4371

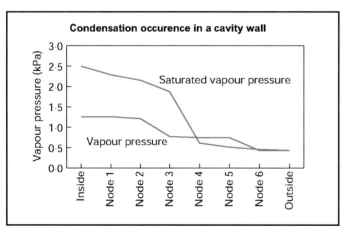

Step 4. This shows that condensation will form at nodes 4 and 5 (where the pink line is below the blue on the graph, highlighted in the table). In practice, condensation could begin to form in the insulation near the cavity; this could be a problem. The method must be repeated to check that condensation will not occur elsewhere.

Taking from the interior surface to node 4 and from node 5 to the exterior surface separately, the method is followed again.

For the section up to node 4, the temperatures will remain the same, but the vapour pressures will have to be recalculated using:

$$P_{vn} = P_{vsi} - \left(\left((P_{vsi} - P_{v4}) \times \sum_{si}^{n} G \right) ÷ \sum_{si}^{se} G \right)$$

Using:

$$P_{v4} = P_{s4} = 0·6182 kPa$$

Table for comparing P_v and P_s up to node 4.

		t (°C)	P_v (kPa)	P_s (kPa)
Inside	-	21·00	1·2580	2·4860
Node 1	Inside/plaster	19·63	1·2580	2·2846
Node 2	Plaster/blockwork	18·70	1·2002	2·1557
Node 3	Blockwork/insulation	16·47	0·6442	1·8720
Node 4	Insulation/cavity	0·16	0·6182	0·6182

Again for the section from node 5, the temperatures will remain the same and the vapour pressures will have to be recalculated, this time using:

$$P_{vn} = P_{vsi} - \left(\left((P_{vs} - P_{vse}) \times \sum_{si}^{n} G \right) ÷ \sum_{si}^{se} G \right)$$

Using:

$$P_{v5} = P_{s5} = 0·5220 kPa$$

Table for comparing P_v and P_s from node 5.

		t (°C)	P_v (kPa)	P_s (kPa)
Node 5	Cavity/brickwork	-1·89	0·5220	0·5220
Node 6	Brickwork/outside	-3·32	0·4371	0·4632
Outside	-	-4·00	0·4371	0·4371

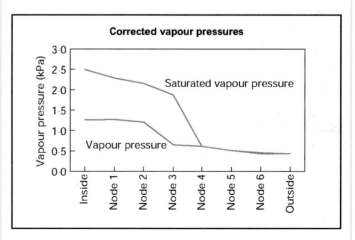

This shows that condensation will not occur anywhere else, as no other nodes have a vapour pressure greater than the saturated vapour pressure. Condensation will only occur where the pink and blue lines meet.

© BSRIA BG 30/2003

H4 CONDENSATION RISK

References:

CIBSE Guide A, *Environmental Design,* Section 7, 1999, ISBN 0 900 953 969

CIBSE Guide C, *Reference Data,* Section 1, 2001, ISBN 7506 5360 4

Building Regulations Approved Document Part F – Ventilation: 1995 Edition, amended 2000, ISBN 0 11752 932 X

BRE, *Thermal Insulation: Avoiding Risks,* BR 262, BRE Scotland, 2002 edition, ISBN 1 86081 515 4

DESIGN WATCHPOINTS

1. A variety of outside temperatures may need to be looked at, not just the design temperature. This will provide the level of outside temperature at which condensation will occur.
2. British Standards BS5250:1989 (1995) *Code of Practice for Control of Condensation in buildings* suggests that condensation risk calculations for the UK, should be carried at 5°C outdoor to 15°C indoor. Other British Standards give suggestions for serious exposure, for example *BS6279:1982 Code of Practice for flat roofs with continuously supports coverings,* which suggests -5° to 20°C. The values you use must be confirmed by your senior engineer.
3. Wherever possible, base the calculations on the data from the actual manufacturer of the materials being used, as values such as thermal and vapour resistances may differ significantly.
4. Ensure that the U value of any structure complies with the *Building Regulations* where appropriate, and notify the relevant party if it does not.
5. Notwithstanding the above calculations, problems with damp and moisture ingress can also occur through poor construction standards and techniques.
6. When there is a serious risk of condensation, a vapour barrier can be applied. In such a case, advice should be sought from senior personnel.

H5 HEAT LOSS

Overview

The heat loss value of a room or building is a measure of the amount of heat or energy that is lost from that space, and hence needs to be replaced by a heating system to maintain a particular internal temperature or comfort level.

The calculation of heat loss is based around the relationships between the following factors:

- External temperature
- Internal temperature
- Dimensions of the various building elements
- Thermal transmittance of the building elements
- Infiltration rate to the space

Design information required

Outside air temperature °C

The value to be used as the lowest outside temperature that can be reached and the design internal temperatures still be achieved. It will vary with geographical location and exposure. (*CIBSE Guide A*, section 2)

Inside dry resultant design temperature °C

The required temperature within the room or space (*CIBSE Guide A*, section 1).

Dimensioned plan or drawing

A plan from which the areas of various building elements, such as walls and floors, can be measured and calculated (from the architect or surveyor).

U values W/m^{2}K

The thermal transmittance is expressed in terms of the U value for a particular building element or surface (*CIBSE Guide A*, section 3).

Infiltration rate

The rate at which external air is introduced into the space in air changes per hour (ach^{-1}). (*CIBSE Guide A*, section 4)

More general design information is contained in *TN 15/2001 Rules of thumb*, available from BSRIA.

Calculation procedure

Step 1. Determine the area of each construction element and work out the product of the area and the previously determined U value for each. If a wall is an internal partition, the U value must be adjusted (just for that wall) as follows:

$$U' = U\left((t_c - t_c') \div (t_c - t_{ao})\right)$$

Where:

U' = adjusted U value (W/m²K)

U = U value (W/m²K)

t_c = dry resultant temperature in room (°C)

t_c' = dry resultant temperature at the opposite side of the partition (°C)

t_{ao} = outside air temperature (°C)

If t_c' is larger than t_c, then the adjusted U value will be negative and will represent a heat gain.

Step 2. Calculate the ventilation conductance of the room:

$$C_v = N\,V \div 3$$

Where:

C_v = ventilation conductance (W/K)

N = air changes per hour (/h)

V = volume of the room (m³)

Step 3. Two correction factors, F_{1cu} and F_{2cu}, are needed to calculate the total heat loss:

$$F_{1cu} = \frac{3\left(C_v + 6\sum A\right)}{\sum(AU) + 18\sum A + 1\cdot5R\left(3C_v - \sum(AU)\right)}$$

$$F_{2cu} = \frac{\sum(AU) + 18\sum A}{\sum(AU) + 18\sum A + 1\cdot5R\left(3C_v - \sum(AU)\right)}$$

Where:

R = radiant fraction of the heat source (see Table 5.4, *CIBSE Guide A*)

$\sum A$ = total area through which heat flow occurs (m²)

$\sum(AU)$ = sum of the products of surface area and corresponding thermal transmittance (W/K)

Step 4. Calculate the total heat loss:

$$Q_t = \left[F_{1cu} x \sum(AU) + F_{2cu} x C_v\right] x (t_c - t_{ao})$$

Where:

Q_t = total heat loss (W)

t_c = dry resultant temperature (°C)

t_{ao} = outside air temperature (°C)

Example

Below is a small factory that is to be heated to a dry resultant temperature of 21°C. The site is subject to normal conditions of exposure, and will be heated using multi-column radiators.

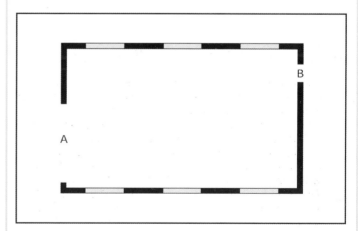

Internal dimensions: 12 m x 7 m x 4 m

Glazing: 2 m x 1·5 m (6 off)

Door A: 4 m x 3·5 m

Door B: 1 m x 2 m

U Value of floor: 0·5 W/m²K

U Value of roof: 0·25 W/m²K

U Value of external walls: 0·55 W/m²K

U Value of glazing: 3·5 W/m²K

U Value of doors: 3 W/m²K

An infiltration rate of 1 air change per hour is assumed for this example. The external design temperature is –4°C.

© BSRIA BG 30/2003

H5 HEAT LOSS

Step 1. This shows the area, U value and the products of both for each surface in the factory:

Surface	Area, A (m²)	U Value, U (W/m²K)	AU (W/K)
Floor	84	0·5	42
Roof	84	0·25	21
Walls	118	0·55	64·9
Glazing	18	3·5	63
Doors	16	3	48
	$\Sigma A = 320$		$\Sigma(AU) = 238·9$

Step 2. Calculate the ventilation conductance:

$C_v = 1 \times (12 \times 7 \times 4) \div 3$

$C_v = 112 \text{ m}^3/\text{h}$

Step 3. Calculate factors F_{1cu} and F_{2cu}:

$$F_{1cu} = \frac{3 \times (112 + 6 \times 320)}{238·9 + 18 \times 320 + 1·5 \times 0·2 \times (3 \times 112 - 238·9)}$$

$F_{1cu} = 1·0111$

$$F_{2cu} = \frac{(238·9 + 18 \times 320)}{238·9 + 18 \times 320 + 1·5 \times 0·2 \times (3 \times 112 - 238·9)}$$

$F_{2cu} = 0·9952$

Step 4. Calculate the total heat loss:

$Q_t = (1·0111 \times 238·9 + 0·9952 \times 112) \times (21 - -4)$

$Q_t = 353·01 \times 25$

$Q_t = 8·825 \text{ kW}$

References:

CIBSE Guide A, *Environmental Design,* Chapters 1,2,3 and 4, 1999, ISBN 0 900 953 969
BSRIA, *Rules of Thumb,* TN 15/2001, BSRIA 2001, ISBN 086022 587 9

See also:

Sheet H2 Infiltration
Sheet H3 U values
Sheet H8 Boiler sizing
Lawrence Race G, *Design Checks for HVAC – A Quality Control Framework for Building Services Engineers* – sheet 24, AG 1/2002, BSRIA 2002, ISBN 0 86022 589 5

DESIGN WATCHPOINTS

1. Use the dimensions shown on the drawings wherever possible rather than scaling from the drawing, as the drawing may become distorted while being copied.
2. Wherever possible, base the calculations on the U values of the actual materials or products to be used.
3. As a minimum requirement, the U values shall comply with the current edition of the *Building Regulations* if the project is to be constructed within the UK.
4. If an adjacent room is warmer than the room being calculated, there may be a heat gain to the room.
5. If different rooms in a building are different temperatures, the heat loss for each room will have to be calculated separately, and then all summed to calculate the total heat loss.
6. If the building is to be continuously occupied, you may consider some reduction in heat loss due to gains from the occupants, lighting and machinery (small power loads).

H6 PLANT HEATING LOAD

Overview
The plant heating load, as the name suggests, is the total heating requirement for a building. The plant heating load consists of:

Fresh air load
Fresh air is introduced into a space to reduce the concentration of contaminants in a space. This includes odours and CO_2 levels. The fresh air load arises from the fresh air intake being conditioned to the required supply air set-points. The fresh air load will depend on the type of system used (for example heat recovery, maximum re-circulation or full fresh air), and the amount of fresh air required to suit the use and conditions within the building, (such as smoking or non smoking office); see Table 1.10 *CIBSE Guide A*.

System losses/gains
One example is fan gains, where the temperature of the air passing through the fan can be raised by between 1-3°C. The temperature difference between the air in the duct and the air surrounding the duct may also result in some heat transfer, which can create the need for extra insulation and therefore raise capital costs.

Infiltration heat loss
This is the heat loss due to outside air entering a space and warm air escaping from the space due to factors such as external wind pressure and temperature differences between inside and outside. The infiltration rate can increase significantly if the room is under negative pressure for example if the mechanical ventilation extract exceeds supply provision either deliberately such as in toilet ventilation or by poor design or poor commissioning. Infiltration into a building will vary depending on the airtightness of the building. The *Building Regulations Approved Document Part L2* requires all new buildings with a gross floor space above 1000 m^2 to be tested for air permeability. The *Approved Document Part L2* gives guidance on how to comply with the *Regulations* whether the building is above or below 1000 m^2.

Fabric heat loss
This is the heat lost through the fabric of the building, the fabric being the building elements such as walls, glazing, roofs and floors.

Zone heating load
The zone load is the total heat loss for a room, or group of rooms, consisting of the fabric and infiltration losses. Typically there is no diversity applied to a room load, so the heat emitter is sized to overcome the total calculated zone load.

Pre heat capacity
Once all the heat losses have been determined, a pre-heat capacity may be added to establish the required boiler capacity. This is discussed in sheet H8 Boiler sizing.

HWS
(If required).

Diversity
The plant heating load is generally made up of the total of the zone loads with a diversity factor applied. This diversity element will vary from building to building, but is intended to reflect the use of the building. In other words one zone of a building may be an office area that is occupied for nine hours a day, while another zone may be a factory area that operates 24 hours a day. A diversity factor is applied to the heating plant to allow for this. This is dealt with in more detail in the sheet H8 Boiler Sizing. (See watchpoints.)

Design information required
Heat losses
Heat losses in terms of each individual zone as well as for the building as a whole.

Use of the building
This will have an impact on the simultaneous heating load of the building.

Heating systems to be used
The types of systems that will be used to meet the heat load, for example a radiator system and fresh air supply system, will have a different heating load to an all air heating system.

Design approach
The plant heating load is determined by adding up the individual heat losses, such as fabric heat loss and infiltration loss, and fresh air load. This is dealt with in more detail in the sheet H5 Heat loss.

References
Building Regulations Approved Document Part L2, 2002, ISBN 0 11753 610 5
CIBSE Guide A, *Environmental Design,* 1999, ISBN 0 900 953 969

See also:
Sheet H2 Infiltration
Sheet H5 Heat loss
Sheet H8 Boiler sizing
Sheet C4 Ventilation – Fresh air requirements
Sheet C5 Supply air quantity and condition

Lawrence Race G, *Design Checks for HVAC – A Quality Control Framework for Building Services Engineers* – sheet 24: Heat Loss, AG 1/2002, BSRIA 2002, ISBN 0 86022 589 5

DESIGN WATCHPOINTS

1. Some computer programmes only include heat losses in their heating loads and do not include fresh air loads unless this information is specifically entered.
2. Diversity factors are complex. For example, the infiltration related heat losses for the building are not the simple summation of individual room losses due to variations in wind velocity and direction. Advice should be sought from a service engineer.

H7 RADIATOR SIZING

Overview

The most common form of heating in domestic and non-domestic buildings is by radiators. This is an inaccurate term as radiators actually provide most of their heat in the form of convection, with a relatively small part by radiation.

Generally, a radiator or radiators are selected to overcome the calculated heat loss of a room. Other considerations such as the available height and space to mount the emitters, or architectural or aesthetic considerations, will all have a bearing on the final selection.

Radiators are typically made from steel, cast-iron or aluminium, and there are number of different configurations which most manufacturers produce. These include the following types:

Single panel

These are exactly what the name suggests - a single panel emitter.

Double panel

These are formed by placing two single panels back to back. This increases the output without requiring additional wall space.

Single-panel convector

This is a single-panel radiator with an additional finned element fitted to the back. This has the effect of increasing the surface area of the emitter, and hence the output.

Double-panel, single convector

This is a double-panel radiator with the additional finned element fitted between them to increase the output.

Double-panel, double convector

This configuration provides the greatest output due to the large amount of surface area obtained by having two panel radiators fitted together, each with a finned element.

All types of radiators, are available in a variety of sizes, with standard heights and almost any length. Special non-standard units can be made to order.
Radiators can be used with a variety of water temperatures to suit the application, but the data produced by the manufacturer detailing the output of their particular products will have been based on particular operating conditions. These figures need to be corrected by the application of factors to obtain the output data for the required use.

BS EN 442 details set conditions to which radiators should be tested to provide certified output figures, and such tests must be carried out by authorised test organisations. The manufacturer will then provide a series of correction factors for use with operating conditions other than those specified in the standard.

Design information required

Heat losses

The radiator/s must be sized to overcome the heat loss from the room.

Room design internal temperature

The room temperature is required to calculate the correction factor for radiator outputs.

Water flow and return temperatures

The average water temperature is required to determine the radiator outputs. Flow and return temperatures of $82^{\circ}C$ and $71^{\circ}C$ are often used but other temperatures may be suitable for the application.

Radiator manufacturers' data

Output and general performance of radiators varies from one manufacturer to another. They will also provide the appropriate correction factors for different operating conditions.

Available space

Radiators must be selected to fit into the space available.

Building construction details

These details will help to place the radiators in the most advantageous positions, such as under windows, to offset down-draughts and the effect of cold radiation.

Pre-heat factor

When sizing the heating plant a pre-heat factor also known as a boost margin or plant ratio may be included. This may help overcome any additional loss due to poor construction, use of alternative materials to those assumed at design stage or provide some spare capacity to aid initial warm-up. The pre-heat factor is often expressed as a percentage of the calculated heat loss. This pre-heat factor is normally included in the sizing of the boiler but has sometimes been historically included in the radiator or emitter sizing. An alternative to increasing the size of an emitter or boiler for pre-heating is to increase the flow temperature.

> ➤ **Design tip:** For occupied spaces consider omitting the emission from pipes in radiator sizing calculations. Any emission from the pipes to the occupied space is useful heating. As long as the total design capacity is available, it does not matter that some comes from the pipes and some from the emitters. This will also reduce pipe size, and reduce unnecessary system over sizing.

Key design inputs

- Zone heating loads, in kW
- Design flow and return temperatures, in $^{\circ}C$
- Internal design condition, in $^{\circ}C$

© BSRIA BG 30/2003

H7 RADIATOR SIZING

Design outputs

- A schedule of radiators with water and surface temperature, connection and valve requirements, and sufficient data for manufacturer selection
- Control requirements
- Commissioning strategy statement
- Relevant specification clauses

Design approach

1. Determine the room heat loss to be overcome by the radiator. This can be found by following the procedures detailed in the appropriate data sheets.
2. Calculate the mean water temperature (mwt) as the average of the flow and return temperatures

$$mwt = \frac{\text{flow temperature} + \text{return temperature}}{2}$$

3. Subtract the room temperature from the mean water temperature to establish the system temperature difference.
4. Select the appropriate output correction factor for the system temperature difference from the manufacturer's data.
5. Divide the room heat loss by the output correction factor to obtain a corrected required output figure.
6. Select a suitable radiator from the manufacturer's literature, which meets the corrected required output figure.

Example

Select a radiator to suit the following case:

Design data

Room heat loss:
  2750 W
Water temperatures:
  flow 82°C
  return 71°C
Room temperature:
  21°C
Heat output correction factors are given by the equation
$Q = k\Delta t^{1.33}$ in the table below.

System temperature difference °C	Correction factor
40	0·605
45	0·700
50	0·798
55	0·898
60	1·000
65	1·104
70	1·211

Radiator output data (radiator height: 600 mm)

Sections	Length mm	Output W		
		Type 1	Type 2	Type 3
28	1120	929	1361	1988
32	1280	1056	1552	2265
36	1440	1182	1741	2542
40	1600	1307	1930	2818
44	1760	1432	2119	3094
48	1920	1556	2308	3369
52	2080	1680	2496	3644
56	2240	1803	2683	3918
60	2400	1926	2871	-
64	2560	2049	3058	-
68	2720	2171	3245	-
72	2880	2293	3431	-

Radiator type 1: single panel
Radiator type 2: single panel with convector
Radiator type 3: double panel with single convector

Calculation procedure

Step 1. From the design data, the design heat loss for the room is 2750 W.

Step 2. Calculate the mean water temperature;
Mean water temperature (mwt) =

$$\frac{82+71}{2} = 76 \cdot 5°C$$

Step 3. The system temperature difference is;
mean water temperature − room temperature

$$= 76 \cdot 5 - 21 = 55 \cdot 5°C$$

Step 4. Find the output correction factor by interpolating between the figures on the opposite table. As the system temperature difference in this case is equal to 10% above 55°C, then the required factor will be that of the 55°C factor plus 10% of the difference between the 55°C and 60°C factors.

Correction factor for 60°C = 1·000
Correction factor for 55°C = 0·898
Correction factor required for 55·5°C
Interpolate between 1·000 and 0·898.

Therefore:
$$1 \cdot 000 - 0 \cdot 898 = 0 \cdot 102$$
$$60°C - 55°C = 5°C$$
$$\frac{5°C}{0 \cdot 5°C} = 10$$

Ten percent of 0·102 needs to be added to the correction factor for 55°C, hence correction factor for 55·5°C is:

$$0 \cdot 898 + \frac{0 \cdot 102}{10} = 0 \cdot 898 + 0 \cdot 0102 = 0 \cdot 9082$$

© BSRIA BG 30/2003

H7 RADIATOR SIZING

Step 5. To obtain the corrected required output figure:

$$\frac{\text{required output}}{\text{output correction factor}} = \frac{2750}{0\cdot9082} = 3028\,\text{W}$$

Step 6. From the data in the radiator selection chart opposite, the three options available are:

Option 1, single panel with convector radiator:
64 sections, 2560 mm long, 3058 W output

Option 2, double panel radiator with single convector:
44 sections, 1760 mm long, 3094 W output

Option 3, two single panel with convector radiators:
32 sections, 1280 mm long, 1552 W output each.

The final selection will depend on issues including space available, aesthetics and cost.

References

BSI, BS EN 442 – *Specification for Radiators and Convectors*, ISBN 0580257762
BSRIA, *Rules of Thumb*, TN 15/2001, BSRIA 2001, ISBN 086022 587 9
Lawrence Race G, *Design Checks for HVAC – A Quality Control Framework for Building Services Engineers* – sheet 28, AG 1/2002, BSRIA 2002, ISBN 0 86022 589 5

See also:

Sheet H3 U values
Sheet H5 Heat loss
Sheet H6 Plant heating load
Sheet H8 Boiler Sizing
CIBSE Guide B1, *Heating*, 2002, ISBN 1 903 487 200

Manufacturers' literature for output figures and correction factors.

DESIGN WATCHPOINTS

1. When selecting radiators to fit into a particular space, remember to make sufficient space allowance for radiator valves or thermostatic radiator valves.
2. Make sure that the surface temperature of the radiators is suitable for the intended use. For example, low surface temperature emitters may be required in healthcare premises.
3. Ensure that the correct fixings are used for securing the radiator to the wall. Some large radiators can weigh in excess of 50 kg.
4. Check radiator pipe connections are as specified by the manufacturer, such as TBOE or BOE as given outputs may depend on connection type.
5. Using the power law $Q = k\Delta t^{1.33}$ removes any need to apply a correction factor and avoids interpolation.

H8 BOILER SIZING

Overview

Boiler plant should be capable of meeting the maximum simultaneous load experienced by the building or site throughout the year. It should be sized and selected to also satisfy the following criteria:

1. To maintain optimum thermal efficiency throughout the operating year.
2. To provide accurate load matching of the plant output to the heat demand.
3. To have sufficient standby capacity to ensure effective operation in times of partial plant failure.
4. To provide spare capacity to meet future needs specified by the client.
5. To have sufficient capacity to meet the pre-heating requirements of the building.

Section 4.7 of *CIBSE Guide B1*, contains more information on additional plant capacities.
Boiler plant needs to meet the requirements of several different load sources:

Heating

The water generated by the boiler plant can be used in a number of different heating system types:

1. Low and medium temperature hot water heating circuits, typically feeding radiators, convectors, radiant panels and underfloor heating manifolds.
2. Air based heating systems including such applications as LTHW frost coils and heater batteries within air handling units, as well as fan coil units and unit heaters.

Domestic hot water

Boiler plant is also used to provide primary energy to a variety of heat exchange equipment generating hot water, generally stored at a lower temperature than the primary circuit, for use in domestic hot water applications. For example:

1. Calorifiers and commercial/industrial water storage equipment where large quantities of domestic hot water are used.
2. Plate heat exchangers – a method of instantaneously generating large quantities of domestic hot water. This approach provides little or no storage capacity.
3. Domestic hot water cylinder – the indirect copper hot water cylinder is the most common source of domestic hot water generation.

Process load

Sometimes, in industrial situations, boiler plant may be required to produce hot water as part of a manufacturing process. This is a more specialist application and is often provided by dedicated boiler plant, and not the type used in general building services systems.

All loads to be met by the boiler plant must be carefully calculated and considered to arrive at the total boiler capacity required. The type, number and arrangement (such as multi boilers or modular boilers) of boilers should be selected to not only meet the load requirement but also be suited to the application and available fuel supply. More details are available in *CIBSE Guide B1*, Section 5.1.2.

Design information required
Heating load
The total heating load to be met by the plant.

Domestic hot water load
The primary load necessary to deal with the maximum simultaneous domestic hot water load.

Process load
Any process load that may be supplied from the boiler plant.

Details of building usage
For example, 24 hours occupancy of certain areas to assist in establishing diversity and peak demand.

Diversity
Generally a diversity factor can be applied to plant sizing if the plant is to operate continuously, or if one service can be sacrificed or reduced at times to help satisfy the peak demands of another. (See Design Watchpoint 1.)

Building characteristics
The form and weight of the building is important in order to determine its inertia. This has a large effect on the additional plant capacity that may need to be provided in the form of pre-heat to allow intermittent operation. (See Design Watchpoint 2.)

Calculation procedure
Step 1. Calculate the peak or maximum simultaneous demand of the various systems to be supplied by the boiler plant. This involves examining the loads and their operating times to arrive at the peak requirement.

Step 2. Apply diversity to the total load. This may be relevant if the plant is operating continuously, or if it is thought that the performance of one system can be reduced for short periods to lower the overall plant capacity. A typical example may be that the domestic hot water load can be suppressed if the heating demand is at full load at the same time.

Step 3. Apply a plant factor for preheating capacity if the building services are to operate intermittently. Information is given in a number of sources including *CIBSE, Guide A,* section 5.8.3.3, and *BSRIA Laboratory Report No. 26, Intermittent Heating.* Unnecessary excess capacity is inefficient and can result in poor part-load operation with certain boiler and air-circuit types. (See Design Watchpoint 3.)

Step 4. Calculate the required installed load of the plant from steps 1 to 3 above.

© BSRIA BG 30/2003

H8 BOILER SIZING

Step 5. Determine the plant arrangement to best suit the load requirements considering the use of multiple or modular boilers. The plant should be selected to operate at maximum possible efficiency during both the summer and winter loads. Where the seasonal load variations are large, separate plant may be selected for each season, but connected to the same distribution network.

Example
Determine the boiler sizing for a building with the following load requirements.

Design data
Heating systems
Radiator system load: 150 kW
Air handling unit load: 50 kW
Domestic hot water load: 100 kW

Occupancy pattern
Radiator system:	09·00 h – 18·00 h
Air handling unit:	09·00 h – 18·00 h
Domestic hot water	08·00 h – 10·00 h
	16·00 h – 18·00 h

Step 1. Maximum simultaneous load. First, determine the maximum simultaneous load for the systems:

The maximum demand occurs between 09.00 h and 10.00 h, and then again between 16.00 h and 18.00 h, and is:

Radiator load + AHU load + DHWS

$= 150 \text{ kW} + 50 \text{ kW} + 100 \text{ kW} = 300 \text{ kW}$

However, during the summer when there is no heating load, the maximum load is only;

DHWS load = 100 kW

> **Design tip:** An HWS system does not have to be supplied by the main boiler system; alternatives are available such as a separate summer boiler or a separate gas/oil fired HWS generator.

Step 2. Diversity – As the use of the building dictates that the domestic hot water and heating should be available throughout the times stated in the design criteria, and as the plant is operated intermittently, there is no scope for applying diversity in this case.

Step 3. Plant factor for pre-heat – Applying a pre-heat factor F_3 of 1.2 (minimum suggested value *CIBSE Guide A* section 5.8.3.3) to the radiator heating load to allow for admittance of the structure. This gives a required heating plant capacity of:

150 kW x 1·2 = 180 kW

Using equation 5.50 in section 5.8.3.3 of *CIBSE Guide A* gives details on how to calculate F_3.

No such factor is required for the domestic hot water as the criteria which determine the power required vary very little. The plant size for the domestic hot water is simply a function of the volume of water to be heated through a given temperature range in a given time. As such, no pre-heat capacity is required.

Step 4. Installed load requirements – The installed load requirements for the two systems are:

Heating: 180 kW
AHU Load: 50 kW
Domestic hot water: 100 kW
Total maximum installed load capacity: 330 kW

Step 5. Plant arrangement – The two systems indicate a clear difference in load requirements throughout the year. Therefore, in order to operate plant as close to maximum efficiency as possible, a plant selection strategy of providing a degree of separate plant for each system may be appropriate.

For instance, to meet the heating load of 230 kW, a possible strategy would be to install two boilers, each at half the load for example 115 kW. This not only meets the load requirements but also provides some degree of safety should one of the boilers be out of use due to failure or routine maintenance.

In cases where a preheat factor has not been applied, boilers are often selected to provide 60% of the total load, for example two boilers at 138 kW each. (See Design Watchpoint 4.)

Assuming the boilers selected have a burner turn- down ratio of 50% (giving 50% output), this gives four combinations of plant capacities to deal with part load conditions:

One boiler at 50%, one boiler off = 75 kW,
One boiler at 100% full, one boiler off = 150 kW,
One boiler at 100%, one boiler at 50% = 225 kW,
Two boilers at 100% = 300 kW.

Where modulating burners are used, the output is almost infinitely variable from a minimum setting right up to full load. With this arrangement, part-load efficiencies tend to be higher than for two-stage or on/off burners.

For the domestic hot water service, a single boiler of 100 kW would be suitable. This third boiler can operate on its own throughout the summer season, with the heating boilers available as back-up should the DHWS boiler fail.

Therefore, the selected plant arrangement for this example is:

Two boilers at 150 kW each
One boiler at 100 kW

© BSRIA BG 30/2003

H8 BOILER SIZING

Design tips

➤ When sizing primary circuit pipework, use the flow rate which corresponds to the maximum boiler capacity that is available, as that could conceivably be passing through the system.

➤ Make sure that the controls strategy adopted takes account of the way you want the plant to operate. For example when domestic hot water is called for in the summer period, a DHWS boiler should be fired and not one of the heating boilers. Control strategies for heating systems are available in the *BSRIA AG 7/98 Library of system control strategies.*

➤ When designing flue systems for the boilers, ensure that the flue will work adequately for all load conditions.

➤ Provide back-end protection and controls so that when a boiler starts up hot water is circulated to the rear of the boiler near the flue. This will minimise formation of condensate from the flue gases.

➤ Always ensure adequate ventilation in the plant area to satisfy the combustion requirement of the boilers. Insufficient or restricted air flow will reduce the output and efficiency of the plant.

➤ When selecting boiler plant, always allow adequate space for maintenance. Installation should be strictly in accordance with the manufacturer's instructions. This will depend on the overall available space allowed by the architect for plant room areas.

➤ Ensure that adequate space is available for the plant selected. In areas with restricted space or access, modular-type units may be required.

➤ Check any necessary requirements with specific products, for example continuous water flow and shunt pumps. This may have an affect on the overall hydraulic design of the system.

➤ Check that any margins added to the boiler are not repeated in any allowances on the room or emitter loads.

➤ Where multi-boiler plant is installed, provide flue dampers to avoid heat losses to atmosphere from the boilers when they are offline.

References:

CIBSE Guide A, *Environmental Design,* Section 5.8.3.3, 1999, ISBN 0 900 953 969
CIBSE Guide B1, *Heating,* Section 5.1.2, 2002, ISBN 1 903 487 200
Martin A J, Banyard C P, *Library of System Control Strategies,* AG 7/98, BSRIA 1998, ISBN 0 86022 497 X
Lawrence Race G, *Design Checks for HVAC – A Quality Control Framework for Building Services Engineers* – sheet 49, AG 1/2002, BSRIA 2002, ISBN 0 86022 589 5

See also:

Sheet H2 Infiltration
Sheet H5 Heat loss
Sheet H6 Plant heating load
Sheet H9 Flue sizing
Sheet C4 Ventilation – Fresh air requirements
Sheet W6 Water system pressurisation
Design watchpoints

DESIGN WATCHPOINTS

1. Restrictions in the choice of flue that can be used may influence the type of boiler used in the system. *CIBSE Guide B1,* Section 5.1.2 gives details on the types of boilers available and their suitability for different applications.
2. Pre-heat is usually considered with the boiler capacity rather than the radiator capacity, but not both.
3. Applying a plant factor for preheating capacity effectively adds a margin to the system size and should be carefully considered. Check if any margins have been added elsewhere in the design and avoid the use of duplicate margins.
4. Boiler selection will also depend on standard boiler sizes available for example two boilers at 150 kW.

H9 FLUE SIZING

Overview

Flue or chimney sizing is required to allow the products of combustion to be exhausted from the boiler. The flue disperses the exhaust gases to prevent air pollution in confined spaces and dilute the gases to an acceptable level normally to open space.

Calculations on this sheet will give a preliminary height and size of the flue. The final design should normally be carried out by a specialist (such as a flue manufacturer), taking into account pressure drops and flue resistance.

To achieve this, the flue or chimney design must take into consideration many aspects of the system and building in which it is housed. These include whether the flue/chimney is free standing or adjacent to a building, and whether it is a single or multi-flue system. All of these will affect the overall height of the flue.

Once the height is determined the flue area needs to be selected. This will require details of the fuel to be burned along with velocities and friction losses within the flue. The selected flue area must provide the highest possible flue-gas velocity and the smallest cooling area. This must also take into consideration the available draught. Total resistance of the flue/chimney is compared to the available chimney draught. If the residual chimney draught is excessive then the flue areas can be recalculated using higher flue-gas velocities.

Design information required

- Fuel type with details of calorific value and the percentage sulphur content.
- Type and rated output of the boiler.
- Overall thermal efficiency of the boiler based on gross calorific value.
- Boiler flue-gas outlet conditions at both high and low fire. This should include gas outlet temperatures and percentages of carbon dioxide.
- Draught requirements at the boiler outlet at high and low fire.
- Height of installation above sea level. Gas volumes are increased by approximately 4% for every 300 m above sea level. For installations at more than 600 m above sea level allowances must be made in specifying volumes of forced and induced fans.
- Location of plant and the character of the surroundings, such as topography, the height of any buildings that may surround any plant, prevailing wind direction and velocities and the position of the boiler (such as a basement or roof top location).
- Winter and summer extremes of ambient temperature.
- Proposed chimney construction to assess the cooling effect on gases.

Calculation procedure for sulphur bearing fuels

Step 1. Use $q_m = 100\varphi \div (\eta h_g)$

Where:

q_m = maximum fuel burning rate (kg/s)
φ = the rated boiler output (kW)
η = thermal efficiency of the boiler(%)
h_g = the calorific value of the fuel (kJ/kg)

Step 2. Find the maximum sulphur dioxide emission for fired equipment:

$E_m = K_1 q_m S$

Where:

E_m = the maximum SO_2 emission (g/s)
S = the sulphur content of the fuel (%)
K_1 = a constant – 20 for oil firing, 18 for coal firing

Alternatively use $E_m = K_2 \times \varphi \div \eta$

Where K_2 is a constant that can be found from *CIBSE Guide B1*, table A2.1.

Step 3. If E_m is more than 0.38 g/s, use *CIBSE Guide B1*, page A2-1 to determine the category of the chimney, and use figure A2.1 to find the uncorrected chimney height. For fuel of more than 2% sulphur content, multiply this value by 1.1.

Step 4. If the value found in Step 3 exceeds 2.5 times the height of the building, then that is the height of the chimney. If it is not, substitute into the following formula:

$$H = (0.56\, h_a + 0.375\, h_b) + 0.625\, h_c$$

Where:

H = final chimney height (m)
h_a = building height or greatest length, whichever is the lesser (m)
h_b = building height (m)
h_c = uncorrected chimney height in metres found in Step 3

Step 5. If the emission of sulphur dioxide is less than 0.38 g/s:

a) Assess the height of the buildings through which the chimney passes or to which it is attached.
b) Add 3 m to this height
c) Where the particular building is surrounded by higher buildings, the height of the latter must be taken into consideration as above
d) Select a trial flue-gas velocity (from *CIBSE Guide B1*, table A2.3) and calculate the flue and chimney resistance
e) Compare this with the available chimney draught (figure A2.2) and adjust the chimney height to suit, recalculating if necessary.

© BSRIA BG 30/2003

H9 FLUE SIZING

Calculation procedure for non-sulphur bearing fuels

Procedure – single chimneys

Step 1. Assess the boiler plant heat input rate.

Step 2. When dealing with a single freestanding chimney, read off the corresponding height from figure A2.3 in *CIBSE Guide B1* (the left hand side of chart).

Step 3. When dealing with single chimneys that pass through or adjacent to buildings, read the height off figure A2.3 in *CIBSE Guide B1* (right hand side of chart). This should then be added to the building height to give the final chimney height.

Procedure – multi-chimneys

Step 1. Work out the final chimney height as previously shown.

Step 2. Determine the freestanding height of each chimney if each is considered to be alone and completely freestanding (left hand side of figure A2.3 in *CIBSE Guide B1*).

Step 3. Express the separation (distance) 's' between each pair as a multiple of the free standing height of the smaller chimney determined in 2.

Step 4. Using the ratio of s to H_f (smaller chimney) determined in 3, read off the height correction factor 'h' from figure A2.4 in *CIBSE Guide B1*.

Step 5. Calculate the required increase in height:
$$\Delta H_2 = h \times H_f \text{ (taller chimney)}$$

Step 6. Repeat these steps for each combination of pairs of chimneys.

Step 7. Add the largest increase in height (ΔH_2) found to the final height of each chimney.

Step 8. Check that the overall height of each chimney provides the required combustion draught.

Calculation procedure for flue area

Before starting any calculations the following information is required:

Step 1. Flue-gas volume flow-rates to be handled at full and low fire conditions according to the temperature involved at the particular boiler outlet.

Flue-gas velocity – select a reasonable velocity for the plant from table A2.3 in *CIBSE Guide B1*.

Step 2. The equivalent area needs to be calculated from:
$$A = \frac{q_f}{v}$$
where:

A = area equivalent m^2 (table A2.4 in *CIBSE Guide B1*)

q_f = flue gas volume flow rate at full fire (m^3/s)

v = flue gas velocity (m/s)

Step 3. The diameter of the flue can then be calculated from:
$$d = 2\sqrt{(A \div \pi)}$$

Step 4. If the flue to be fitted is a different cross-section (such as rectangular), use figure 4.40 or 4.41 to find the equivalent dimensions. This gives a preliminary size for the flue.

Example
Find the heights and areas of three chimneys on top of a building 10 m high. All boilers burn non-sulphur bearing fuel.

Design data
Boiler A produces 5 MW
Boiler B produces 14 MW
Boiler C produces 9 MW
A to B is 10 m
B to C is 15 m
C to A is 19·5 m
Volume flow rate for A is 4·3 m^3/s
Volume flow rate for B is 12·1 m^3/s
Volume flow rate for C is 7·8 m^3/s

Using the procedure for multi-chimneys:
Step 1. Heights to be added to height of building are:
A – 1·8 m
B – 3·2 m
C – 2·5 m

Therefore the heights of the chimneys (before correction) are:

A – 11·8 m
B – 10·2 m
C – 12·5 m

Step 2. From figure A2.3, freestanding heights are:
A – 4·4 m
B – 7·4 m
C – 6 m

Step 3. Ratio of s to H_r:
AB – 2·27
BC – 2·5
CA – 4·43

Step 4. Height correction factors (h) from figure A2.4
A – 0·24
B – 0·23
C – 0·18

Step 5. Increase in height ($H_r \times h$)
A – 1·056 m
B – 1·702 m
C – 1·08 m

Step 6. Therefore use 1·702 m, as it is the largest increase

Step 7. Final Heights:
A – 11·8 + 1·702 = 13·5 m
B – 13·2 + 1·702 = 14·9 m
C – 12·5 + 1·702 = 14·2 m

© BSRIA BG 30/2003

H9 FLUE SIZING

Using the procedure for calculation of flue area:

Step 1. From table A2.3, flue gas velocity is 4·5 m/s

Step 2. Area Equivalent (A= $q_f \div v$)
A – 0·956 m²
B – 2·689 m²
C – 1·733 m²

Step 3. Diameter (d=2√(A÷π))
A – 1·1 m
B – 1·85 m
C – 1·49 m

Step 4. Therefore the preliminary sizings are:
A – 13·5 m high, diameter 1·1 m
B – 14·9 m high, diameter 1·85 m
C – 14·2 m high, diameter 1·49 m

References

CIBSE Guide B, *Installation and Equipment Data*, 1986, ISBN 0 900 953 306
CIBSE Guide B1, *Heating*, Appendix A2, 2002, ISBN 1 90328 720 0
Clean Air Act (1993), ISBN 0 105 411 930

See also:

Sheet H6 Plant heating load
Sheet H8 Boiler Sizing
Lawrence Race G, *Design Checks for HVAC – A Quality Control Framework for Building Services Engineers* – sheet 49, AG 1/2002, BSRIA 2002, ISBN 0 86022 589 5

DESIGN WATCHPOINTS

1. Designing flue areas and heights correctly is very important due to the health issues surrounding the exhaust gases. Because of this it is recommended that specialists do the final designs.

2. When requesting a design from a specialist certain information will be required. This will include:
   - Surrounding location of chimney/flue
   - Type of fuel used
   - System requirements

3. If however a preliminary design is required for a project, use the procedures listed on pages 34 and 35. These can be found in *CIBSE Guide B1*, Appendix A2 with additional information in Section 5.5.

The following section contains seven building services engineering topic areas related to the design of cooling systems, including cooling loads and plant sizing.

The following two pages contain flow charts of the relevant design and calculation processes.

The first flow chart shows the seven topics within this section.

The second flow chart provides an overview of the process, showing some of the many related topics that need to be considered in the design of cooling systems. The boxes highlighted in blue show an area that is fully or partially covered within one of the seven topic areas in this section, or in the rest of the guidance, with the appropriate reference numbers given.

FLOW CHART 1 – TOPICS WITHIN THIS SECTION

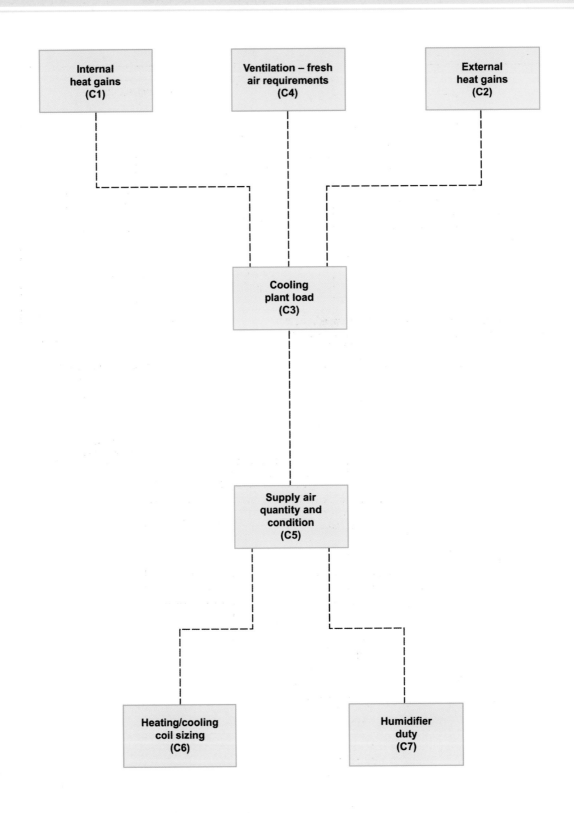

© BSRIA BG 30/2003

FLOW CHART 2 – OVERVIEW OF SYSTEM DESIGN PROCESS

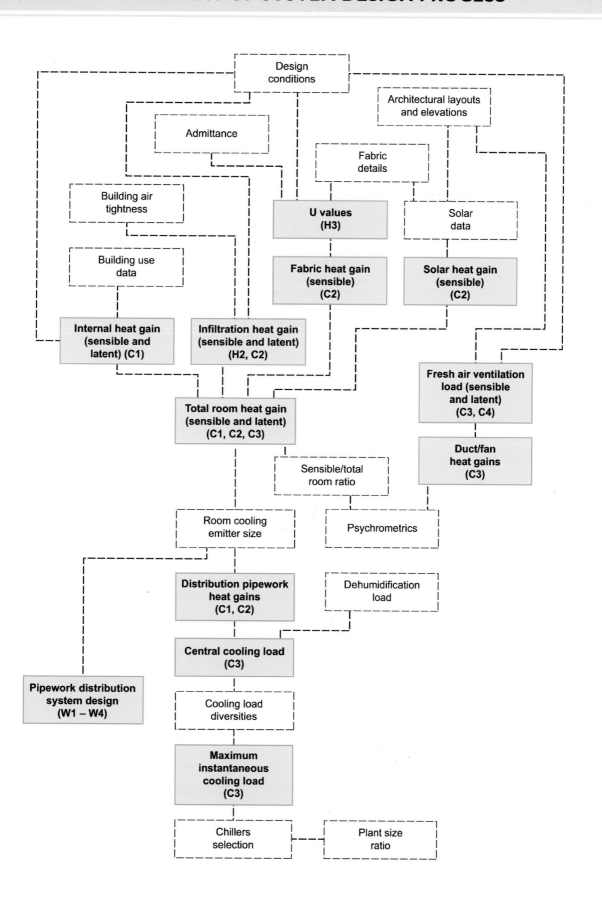

This chart shows the design areas relevant to this design process. Where design areas are wholly or partially discussed in this document the relevant sheet references are given in brackets

© BSRIA BG 30/2003

C1 INTERNAL HEAT GAINS

Overview

When calculating cooling loads, the effect of heat gains needs to be taken into consideration. This includes gains that are generated internally but the source may be external. The internal gains depend on the use of the building and this will need to be clarified before starting any calculations.

Some buildings may have zones or rooms that are maintained at a different temperature to the rest of the building. The individual systems that serve these rooms will need to be sized to take into consideration the gains and losses through internal walls to the rest of the building, likewise the system serving the rest of the building will need to be designed to consider the impact of these individually conditioned spaces.

Design information required

Identifying heat from occupants

Heat emissions from the occupants of a building vary according to the activity of the people within and the conditions (temperature and humidity) in which they are working.

The total heat emission from occupants comprises sensible heat gains and latent heat gains. The sensible heat gains affect the temperature within the space, whereas the latent gains affect the humidity in the space.

Heat emission can vary from 90 W sensible and 25 W latent per person when seated at rest to 190 W sensible and 250 W latent per person for heavy work at 20°C. These figures can be found in Table 6.1 of *CIBSE Guide A*. The three main considerations when dealing with occupancy gains are:

1. Occupancy hours – Is the building used for daytime use only or is it used 24 h/day (such as call centres and hospitals).
2. Number of occupants – The normal number of occupants in the building during occupancy hours. Also include the number of people using the building outside occupancy hours, such as security staff, cleaners and night time staff (although hospitals operate 24 h, they will have reduced number of occupants at night through fewer visitors and administration staff).
3. Activity and number of occupants – This may be fairly difficult to assess particularly where the activities change regularly. Conference rooms, meeting rooms and restaurants will have a varied occupancy from day to day.

Identifying heat from lighting

All of the energy is eventually converted into heat. Different types of lamp will give different heat outputs in both radiant and convective form. The percentage of radiant heat is required when dealing with air and environmental points. The location of the lamp will also have an impact on the direction of the output. A recessed light fitting within a ceiling void will heat the air in the void increasing the ceiling temperature, which in turn will heat the space. If there is significant airflow through the void the heat gains from the lights may be removed. The control gear of the lamp will also contribute heat gains into the space. Manufacturers' data will provide information specific to the lamp and control gear arrangement.

For each type of lamp used, details of the heat output, number of lamps and hours of use are required.

Identifying heat from office machinery and process equipment

The heat gains from all types of machinery will need to be considered. This includes office equipment, lifts and hoists. If a piece of equipment has a name plate which shows it to be 1·5 kW, this does not necessarily mean that 1·5 kW of heat will be dissipated into the space. Either apply a diversity factor to the kW rating (which also has to be reasonable), or use values available in Table 6.6 onwards in *CIBSE Guide A*, or values available in the BSRIA technical note *Small Power Loads* TN 8/92, which give indications of worst case power demand (W) and worst case nameplate ratio percentages for different items that are commonly found in an office.

Key design inputs
- Occupancy and activity details
- Details of proposed lighting scheme
- Details of proposed small power provision

Design outputs
- Schedule of internal gains and sources for each space giving gains from occupants, lighting, small power and other equipment. Gains may also be broken down to give radiant and convective components

References

CIBSE Guide A, *Environmental* Design, Section 6, 1999, ISBN 0 900 953 969

Hejab M, Parsloe C, *Small Power Loads*, TN 8/92, BSRIA 1992, ISBN 0 86022 340 X

See also:

Sheet C2 External gains

Sheet C3 Cooling plant load

Lawrence Race G, *Design Checks for HVAC – A Quality Control Framework for Building Services Engineers* – sheet 18, AG 1/2002, BSRIA 2002, ISBN 0 86022 589 5

DESIGN WATCHPOINTS

1. Don't forget, when calculating heat gains for buildings that are to house animals, the gains per animal need to be included, these are quite different to those of people. Values are available in section 6 Table 6.2 of the *CIBSE Guide A*.

© BSRIA BG 30/2003

C2 EXTERNAL GAINS

Overview

External gains are made up of three different components, solar, conductive (temperature) and convective (airflow). Solar radiation that reaches the earth is in two forms: direct and diffuse.

Diffuse radiation

This occurs when solar radiation is absorbed and reflected from dust and vapours in the atmosphere. Diffuse radiation can also have a heat gain effect on a building by being reflected from other surfaces onto the building.

Direct solar radiation (may be referred to as solar beam)

This occurs when the radiation has a direct effect on the building in other words it is not diffused or reflected. If done by hand solar gain calculations can be lengthy. The amount of gain depends upon the location of the building, the orientation of the building, the angle of any surface of the building, time of day and day of year.

Solar gain occurs through fabric and glazing, and the procedures for calculating each are dealt with differently. With fabrics such as walls, the associated time lag and decrement factor will be needed, whether they are calculated manually or with a computer package. For solar gains through glazing, the glazed area, type of glazing and amount of shading can have a significant impact on the total gains.

Fabric and infiltration

The conduction through the building fabric depends on the U value of the fabric and the Sol-air temperature difference. There will be a time lag that occurs according to the material and thickness of the fabric.

Heat gains from airflow occur in the form of infiltration. Normally this is associated with heat loss, but this depends on whether the outside air temperature is higher or lower than the inside air temperature.

It is important to calculate external heat gains on an hourly basis to identify the peak gains. Again this can be quite lengthy.

Computer programs are available that will calculate the heat gains (and losses) of a building. Input data needs to be correct otherwise a potentially inaccurate result will be given. Details such as building dimensions (internal and external), orientation, fabric construction and design criteria are required. External gains can be calculated with the right information.

Design information required

Solar and conductive gains

Building orientation and location

The location will probably be fixed as the client may already have a plot of land. If the opportunity exists, it is often worth considering the orientation, size and type of glazing as this can have a major impact on comfort, plant size and energy consumption.

Other surrounding buildings will also have an effect on the gains of the building. When the final decision has been made, the details of orientation of walls should be entered into the computer programme.

Building design

The shape of the building and angles of any surface that is not horizontal or vertical will need to be identified.

Building fabric

Details of the construction fabric and U values are required to calculate the heat transfer gains.

Time lags

The programme may require a value for time lags through the building fabric. The time lag is the time it takes for the heat to transfer through the fabric. This will depend on the type of materials used and their thickness.

Decrement factor

This is a function of the thickness and thermal capacitance of an element and has no dimensions. It represents the ability of an element to moderate the extent of a temperature change at one face of the element before it reaches the other. A decrement factor is defined as the variation in the rate of heat flow through the structure due to variations in external heat transfer temperature from its mean value (with the environmental temperature held constant), divided by the steady-state transmittance.

Time lags and decrement factors for different building fabrics can be found in tables 3.54–3.60 in *CIBSE Guide A*.

Air tightness and infiltration

The build quality and therefore air tightness of a building will determine any heat gains due to infiltration. Infiltration is discussed in sheet H2.

References

CIBSE Guide A, *Environmental Designs,* Sections 2 and 5, 1999, ISBN 0 900 953 969

See also:

Sheet C1 Internal heat gains
Sheet C3 Cooling plant load
Lawrence Race G, *Design Checks for HVAC – A Quality Control Framework for Building Services Engineers* – Sheets 20,21 and 25, AG 1/2002, BSRIA 2002, ISBN 0 86022 589 5.
BSRIA, *Rules of Thumb,* TN 15/2001, BSRIA 2001, ISBN 086022 587 9

DESIGN WATCHPOINTS

1. External gain calculations can be done manually but it is a complex process that is prone to user error.
2. Always check the values that are being entered into the computer programme against a reputable source such as *CIBSE* and *British Standards*. Also check that not only are the values reasonable but are appropriate to the building.
3. Check again once all data is entered. Check the inputs and also make sure that any assumptions the program makes are known and correct. It is easy to make unwitting mistakes particularly if the user is unfamiliar with the computer application.
4. Once a result has been determined from the computer program, examine the results to see if they are what would be expected. It may be beneficial to undertake some manual calculations to cross check your results or to use some rules of thumb to check that the answers are in the expected range.
5. Diffuse radiation is often higher during overcast conditions than during clear sky conditions. Peak gains for north zones will usually occur during overcast conditions.

C3 COOLING PLANT LOADS

Overview

A cooling plant load consists of:

Fresh air load

As with heating plant the fresh air load will depend on the use and conditions within the building, e.g. smoking or non smoking office, (see table 1.10 *CIBSE Guide A*), type of installation used such as full fresh air system.

System losses/gains

This will include fan gains. The temperature of the air passing through a fan can be raised 1-3°C, and the temperature difference between the air in the duct and the air surrounding the duct may result in some heat transfer. This may have implications on the required level of insulation and therefore raise capital costs.

External gains

This is the heat gain through the fabric of the building, the fabric being the building elements such as walls, glazing, roofs and floors. The amount of gain will depend on time of day and seasonal variations (see C2 External gains).

Internal gains

Internal heat gains are all those that occur within the building as explained in sheet C1 Internal heat gains.

Zone load

This is determined from all the heat gains that affect the zone concerned. A zone may consist of several rooms such as all the offices on the east side of a building or be an area within a larger open plan office. Temperature differences between physical barriers of adjacent zones with different set points will also need to be considered as this may result in heat transfer between the two zones.

Peak simultaneous building or zone loads

As the peak loads of each zone will occur at different times of day, it is necessary to establish the time at which the total load for all the zones is at its peak. This is termed the peak simultaneous load.

When determining the cooling load from the heat gains it is important to consider both the sensible and latent heat gain components. Sources of heat such as occupants and catering will have a sensible and latent heat gain effect. The latent heat gains in an area need to be known if the plant is to provide humidity control. If there is to be no allowance for humidity control (such as heating and cooling only) then the cooling coil will be sized to offset only the sensible heat gains. That said, some latent cooling invariably takes place due to the low supply air temperature.

Design information required

Zones

Separating a building into zones enables the temperatures in each zone to be controlled more accurately, particularly when there are varying heat gains between zones. The architect's layout drawings showing the position of windows and columns are required in order to determine the number and size of zones. Each zone will have its own system or part of a system that cools the area, for example AHU's serving each zone, or a group of fan coils for the purpose of cooling only that zone.

Zone heat gains

The heat gains to each area need to be calculated; this will include heat gains through internal walls if there are temperature differences within a single building.

Hourly cooling loads

The zone loads can be calculated on an hourly basis. Plotting the values on a graph will enable the peak simultaneous load to be determined. It is not essential to calculate and plot all the zone cooling loads for each and every hour of the day if the approximate peak time of loads in the building is known. For example if the peak time is likely to be 14.00 h then checking 13.00 h and 15.00 h would be useful to make certain the correct peak time and load is identified. Computer programmes can easily identify the time of the maximum loads.

Example

Consider a theoretical building, which has two zones, east and west. Fifty fan coil units serve each zone. The cooling capacity of each fan coil in the east zone is 1·5 kW each; in the west zone the cooling capacity of each fan coil unit is 2 kW. The total capacity of all the fan coils in the building is 175 kW but the primary cooling system that supplies the fan coils will not need to have a capacity of 175 kW as all the fan coil units will not run at their full capacity at the same time.

The cooling load for each zone is tabulated on an hourly basis and shown in the following table overleaf.

© BSRIA BG 30/2003

C3 COOLING PLANT LOADS

Time 24 h	East zone (kW)	West zone (kW)	Total (kW)
00:00	0	0	0
01:00	0	0	0
02:00	0	0	0
03:00	0	0	0
04:00	0	0	0
05:00	0	0	0
06:00	0	0	0
07:00	20	0	20
08:00	40	20	60
09:00	65	30	95
10:00	75	40	115
11:00	65	60	125
12:00	60	75	135
13:00	55	90	145
14:00	40	100	140
15:00	30	85	115
16:00	20	65	85
17:00	15	55	70
18:00		40	40
19:00		30	30
20:00		20	20
21:00			
22:00			
23:00			

References:
CIBSE Guide A, *Environmental Design,* 1999, ISBN 0 900 953 969

See also:
Sheet H5 Heat loss
Sheet C1 Internal gains
Sheet C2 External gains
Lawrence Race G, *Design Checks for HVAC – A Quality Control Framework for Building Services Engineers* – sheets 17-21, AG 1/2002, BSRIA 2002, ISBN 0 86022 589 5

By adding the loads for the east and west zone at each hour, the building load at each hour can be identified.

From these totals the peak simultaneous load can be found. In this example the peak simultaneous load is 145 kW. The data has been shown in the following graph and clearly shows the peak simultaneous load for the building.

A building may have many areas or zones that will need to be identified and cooling loads calculated in order to find the maximum simultaneous load.

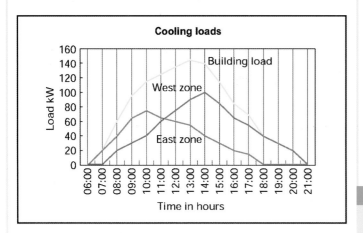

DESIGN WATCHPOINTS

1. Solar gains are not the only gain that may be time dependent. Occupancy of the building may depend on the time of day and the effect of machines and equipment being on standby instead of off when not in use. It is important to consider all the gains on an individual time basis.
2. Some computer programmes only include heat gains in their cooling loads and do not include fresh air loads unless this information is specifically entered.

C4 VENTILATION - FRESH AIR REQUIREMENTS

Overview

Ventilation systems should be designed to meet the requirements of fresh air to the occupants while removing contaminants, as well as providing suitable amounts of air to be able to carry out the process of heating or cooling if required (see sheet C5 supply air quantity and condition).

Fresh air requirements

The amount of fresh air required for any particular project can be determined in a number of ways:

1. Airflow rate per person, expressed as litres/second/person. This is the method generally used for normally occupied spaces such as offices where the quality of the air is important for occupant comfort. Different rates are recommended depending on whether smoking is permitted, or any other sources of contamination present.
2. Airflow rate related to the floor area of the space, expressed in terms of litres per second per metre squared ($l/s/m^2$). This may be used where occupancy numbers are unknown, or where the area is only occupied intermittently.
3. Airflow rate related to the volume of the space as a whole, and expressed in terms of air change rate per hour (ach^{-1}). This term is also often used to specify infiltration rate, and this is discussed in the Infiltration sheet H2. Care is needed not to confuse infiltration with ventilation.

Recommended fresh air supply rates are given in Tables 1.1 and 1.10 in Section 1.3 of *CIBSE Guide A,* and Section 3 of the *CIBSE Guide B2.*

Supply air rate

This term generally refers to the total amount of air introduced into the space, and can be made up of fresh air and re-circulated air. As with the fresh air quantity detailed above, the overall supply air rate can be expressed in a number of ways:

1. **Airflow rate** as calculated to deal with the heating or cooling load, expressed as litres per second (l/s) or cubic metres per second (m^3/s).
2. **Air change rate** as a measure of general ventilation, or for extract systems, and typically expressed as air changes per hour (ach^{-1}). This is also a useful measure for checking other more specific air volume flow calculations, as converting a calculated air volume to an air change rate will give a good indication whether the airflow rate is reasonable. For example, an air volume of $2 \cdot 0$ m^3/s to deal with a cooling load may be reasonable if it equates to, say 2 air changes per hour, but if that value should be 20 air changes per hour, it will prove very problematic to introduce the air into the space effectively through a conventional ductwork system. Noise would also be a likely problem.

Guidance on rates to be used for designing ventilation schemes on this basis are detailed in Table 3.1 in section 3.2.1.1 and Table 3.3 in section 3.2.1.4 of the *CIBSE Guide B2,* and Table 1.1 in Section 1.3 of the *CIBSE Guide A.*

Design information required

Occupancy

When determining fresh air rates in occupied areas such as offices, the number and pattern of occupancy is necessary.

Use of the area

Details of any source of contamination or air quality requirements are relevant.

Size of the space

This is obviously necessary if working to an air change rate criteria, either as a design basis or to use as a checking method.

System design data

Heating or cooling loads will often determine the air flow if they are part of an air conditioning system. Similarly, the design criteria may set the airflow requirements for a ventilation application such as a toilet extract, for example.

Design approach

Fresh air requirements

1. If the fresh air rate for a space is to be based on occupancy, the total fresh air volume will be:

   Air volume (l/s per person) x number of occupants

   This may not necessarily be the total volume of air introduced into the space, but is more likely to be a small component of a larger supply air volume.

   If heating or cooling is to be achieved using an all-air system, then the fresh air component will be part of the required larger supply air volume.

2. Where the fresh air rate is based on the floor area, it will be:

   Air volume ($l/s/m^2$) x floor area (m^2)

Example 1

To calculate the fresh air supply rate for an office where the following criteria apply, (from Table 3.3 in section 3.2.1.4 of the *CIBSE Guide B2*):

Design data

Supply rate (non smoking):	8 l/s/person
Supply rate (smoking):	16 l/s/person
Number of occupants:	150 people

(16 l/s/person relates to 25% of the occupants being smokers but not all smoking at the same time)

C4 VENTILATION - FRESH AIR REQUIREMENTS

Calculation procedure
Total fresh air requirement will be:

8 l/s/person x 150 people
= 1200 l/s or 1·2 m³/s

However, should the fresh air allowance be increased to reflect an allowance for an area where smoking is permitted, the fresh air rate would become:

16 l/s/person x 150 people
= 2400 l/s or 2·4 m³/s

While this doubling of the fresh air volume will not affect the overall volume flow rate of the air into the space (as that will be determined by the cooling load, and assuming that the system is not a full fresh air system), it may have significant implications for plant sizing. The greater volume of outside air will require more energy to heat it or cool it to the supply condition.

Example 2
Calculate the ventilation rate for a museum where the following criteria apply:

Design data
Fresh air supply rate: 8 l/s/person
Number of occupants: 200 people

Calculation procedure
Total fresh air requirement will be:

8 l/s/person x 200 people
= 1600 l/s or 1·6 m³/s

➢ **Design tip:** Use dimensions given on the drawings wherever possible rather than scaling off. Drawings can distort during the copying process resulting in inaccuracies when measuring from the print.

➢ **Design tip:** In an application where air quality is of importance, check that the allowance for fresh air is sufficient to maintain the required air quality.

➢ **Design tip:** In instances where make-up air is required to replace air being extracted, make sure that the path for the make-up air is achievable. The use of an airflow diagram is a simple way to plot air paths and ensure that there is an airflow balance throughout the building that satisfies the design.

➢ **Design tip:** In schemes using a variable supply air volume, ensure that the minimum fresh air requirements are met at all supply air volume conditions.

References:
CIBSE Guide B2, *Ventilation and Air Conditioning*, Section 3.2.1.1, 2001, ISBN 1 903287 16 2
CIBSE Guide A, *Environmental Design*, Section 1.3, 1999, ISBN 0 900 953 969

See also:
Sheet H5 Heat loss
Sheet H6 Plant heating load
Sheet H8 Boiler sizing
Sheet C3 Cooling plant load
Sheet C5 Supply air quantity and condition
Sheet A9 Pressurisation of spaces

Building Regulations Approved Document F – Ventilation: 1995 Edition, amended 2000, ISBN 0 11752 932 X
BSRIA, *Rules of Thumb*, TN 15/2001, BSRIA 2001, ISBN 086022 587 9
Lawrence Race G, *Design Checks for HVAC – A Quality Control Framework for Building Services Engineers* – sheet 6, AG 1/2002, BSRIA 2002, ISBN 0 86022 589 5

C5 SUPPLY AIR QUANTITY AND CONDITION

Overview

Air supply systems are often used to provide heating only, or heating and/or cooling in addition to ventilation requirements, for example in warm air heating or air conditioning all-air systems. Air has a low heat capacity, the amount of air required to carry out heating or cooling is often far in excess of the amount needed to provide fresh air to the occupants. Two of the key system design decisions are therefore to establish both the quantity of air required and the supply condition, that is temperature and moisture content of the supply condition.

These two factors are linked, as a given heating requirement can be met by both a small quantity of air supplied at high temperature or a large quantity of air at a lower temperature.

In practice the choice of system and supply position (high level diffusers, mid level or low level displacement system) may well be dictated by the loads to be met, the configuration of the space and the use of the space. For the purposes of this guidance sheet it is assumed that the decisions on system type and supply outlet type and positions have already been made by a senior engineer.

The choice of supply air temperature and quantity is a fundamental design decision that is necessary for further system design, such as the sizing and selection of distribution systems (ductwork), and of heating and cooling plant, (heating and cooling batteries).

Design information required
Room internal design condition

The room internal design condition (air temperature, and moisture content or percentage saturation) is required as this is the condition that must be achieved by the design heating or cooling system.

Type of system

Details of the proposed supply system, and proposed position and type of supply terminals.

Use of the room or space

Choice of supply condition is normally dictated by comfort criteria –the temperature and velocity at which you can blow air onto people without causing complaint. This in turn will vary with activity and clothing level and occupant position, for example whether they are seated or standing. Occasionally the supply condition will be dictated by process use which may limit supply temperature or velocity.

Key design inputs

- Room air design condition for both summer and winter ie both dry bulb air temperature t_a (°C) and moisture content g (kg/kg). If design condition is given as relative humidity or % saturation then moisture content can be established from psychrometric data. If the design temperature is given as resultant temperature, then a design air temperature will need to be established (see discussion in *CIBSE Guide B2*, Section 3.2.2.1)
- Heating and cooling loads for the space (kW)

Design outputs

- Supply air condition under both heating and cooling, in other words both dry bulb air temperature t_a (°C) and moisture content g (kg/kg)
- Total mass flow rate of supply air (kg/s)

Design approach

Supply air temperature and quantity are linked. In general it is best to have the mass flow rate as small as possible as this will give smaller duct sizes, but this can lead to a large temperature differential between supply temperature and room temperature. As the room design condition is fixed the question is, how low or high can the supply temperature reasonably go?

Limiting factors for supply temperature:

1. The usual limiting factor is comfort, with cooling usually more critical than heating as cool air causes more discomfort. Air velocity and temperature in the occupied zone are critical and can be difficult to predict accurately.
2. Supply outlet type and position, room height and position of occupied zone all relate to acceptable output throw and velocity and the amount of mixing that can occur before air enters the occupied zone
3. Exit temperature from plant. If the primary heat transfer medium is water, the need to keep the fluid in plant above freezing point and below boiling point.
4. High air velocities can result in unwanted noise.

> **Design tip:** Analysis of room air diffusion patterns can be a useful design aid. Although this can be done by computer modelling it is also possible to consider room air diffusion on an intuitive basis by considering information on room configuration, occupant positions and details of outlet types and performance. Think about what happens to air after it leaves the terminal.

Calculation approach

Assume a room with a sensible heat gain/loss (Q_s) and a latent heat gain (Q_l) to be met. Air is supplied at dry bulb temperature t_s and moisture content g_s, and leaves the room at the room dry bulb air temperature t_r and room design moisture content g_r.

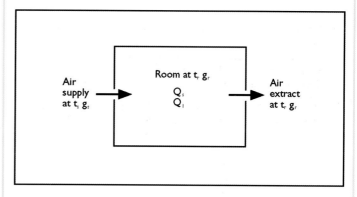

$$Q_s = \dot{m}\, c_p\, \Delta t$$
$$Q_l = \dot{m}\, h_{fg}\, \Delta g$$

© BSRIA BG 30/2003

C5 SUPPLY AIR QUANTITY AND CONDITION

Where:

Q_s = sensible heat gain/loss (kW)

$\dot{m}$ = mass flow rate of supply air (kg/s)

c_p = specific heat capacity of air (kJ/kg K)

Δt = temperature difference between supply air and room air ie $(t_r - t_s)$ for cooling and $(t_s - t_r)$ for heating

Q_l = latent heat gain (kW)

G = moisture content (kg/kg)

h_{fg} = latent heat of evaporation (kJ/kg)

Δg = moisture content differential between supply air and room air, ie $(g_r - g_s)$

Step 1. Select reasonable supply temperature differential for cooling case.

Step 2. Calculate required mass flowrate for cooling. Cross check that ventilation requirements are met and that room air diffusion is acceptable.

Step 3. Check with same mass flow rate to see what the temperature differential is for heating requirements and check whether acceptable for comfort.

Step 4. Recalculate from step 1 if necessary.

Step 5. Use same mass flow rate with the latent heat gain to find the supply moisture content differential.

➤ **Design tip**: If the system is acceptable for cooling then it will usually be acceptable for the heating case. Exceptions are for large heating loads, and of course systems with no cooling, for example with fresh air ventilation only in summer and warm air heating in winter.

➤ **Design tip**: A rough cross-check on room air diffusion acceptability can be done by converting the mass flowrate to an airchange rate for the space and checking against reasonable rules of thumb.

➤ **Design tip**: It is often easier to work using mass-flow rates as these will be used for later plant sizing. Where volume flow rates are required, for example for duct sizing or to cross-check room air-change rates, these can be found from the mass flow rate using values for humid volume or density at the appropriate air condition.

Example 1

Determine a suitable supply air condition and volume flow rate for a small assembly hall for both heating and cooling.

Design data

Room dimensions 15 m x 15 m x 4 m high

Maximum occupancy: 100 people

Room design condition (summer and winter) 21°C db and 50% saturation

Cooling load of 10 kW

Heating load 5 kW

Latent gain (summer and winter) 3 kW

Step 1. Looking at the cooling case first, and considering a ceiling-mounted supply throwing down, a supply temperature differential of 5K is a reasonable first choice.

Step 2.

$$Q_s = \dot{m} c_p \Delta t$$
$$10 = \dot{m} \times 1 \cdot 026 \times 5$$
$$\dot{m} = \frac{10}{1 \cdot 026 \times 5} = 1 \cdot 95 \, \text{kg/s}$$

Cross check 1

Humid volume (v) at an air temperature of 21°C and 50% saturation is $0 \cdot 8434 \, \text{m}^3/\text{kg}$.

Volume flow rate:

= $\dot{m} \times v = 1 \cdot 95 \times 0 \cdot 8434$

= $1 \cdot 64 \, \text{m}^3/\text{s}$

100 occupants require approximately 8 l/s per person fresh air for comfort (no smoking) reference *CIBSE Guide B2*, table 3.3

100 x 8 = 800 l/s = $0 \cdot 8 \, \text{m}^3/\text{s}$

The volume flow rate will therefore be more than sufficient to supply the fresh air requirement. Some recirculation can be used to achieve the required volume flowrate of $1 \cdot 64 \, \text{m}^3/\text{s}$

➤ **Design tip**: Volume flow rate can also be found from $V = m/\rho$ where ρ is the density at the air temperature under consideration.

Alternatively, applying Charles Law relating density and temperature and using values for c_p and ρ at a reference condition of 20°C and 50% sat. then:

$$V_t = \frac{Q_s}{(t_r - t_s)} \times \frac{273 + t_t}{358}$$

Where V_t = Volume flow rate at temperature t_t

This allows temperature values only to be used

Cross check 2

The volume flowrate of $1 \cdot 64 \, \text{m}^3/\text{s}$ gives a room air change rate of:

$$\frac{1 \cdot 64 \times 60 \times 60}{15 \times 15 \times 4} = 6 \cdot 6 \, \text{achr}^{-1}$$

This is within the range of 6-10 air changes per hour recommended as a design strategy in *CIBSE B2* Table 3.6: design requirements: assembly halls and auditoria.

Step 3. Checking under the heating case

$$Q_s = \dot{m} \, c_p \, \Delta t$$
$$5 = 1 \cdot 95 \times 1 \cdot 02 \times \Delta t$$
$$5 = 1 \cdot 95 \times 1 \cdot 02 \times \Delta t$$
$$\Delta t = 2 \cdot 5°C, \text{ which is acceptable}$$

C5 SUPPLY AIR QUANTITY AND CONDITION

Step 4. Not needed

Step 5.

$$Q_l = \dot{m}\, h_{fg}\, \Delta g$$
$$3 = 1{\cdot}95 \times 2450 \times \Delta g$$
$$\Delta g = 0{\cdot}000628 \text{ kg/kg}$$

From psychrometric data, g at 21°C and 50% saturation is 0·007542 kg/kg

The summer supply condition is therefore 16°C and 0·006914 kg/kg

The winter supply condition is therefore 23·5°C and 0·006914 kg/kg

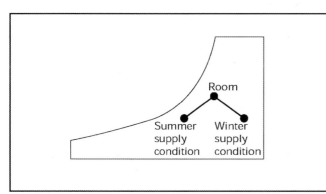

Assumptions

- Humid volume has been taken as a constant value over the operating conditions of the system.

    Note that if the air volume at the supply condition of 16°C is calculated this is:

    $$\dot{m} \times v = 1{\cdot}95 \times 0{\cdot}8279 = 1{\cdot}61 \text{ m}^3/\text{s}$$

    ie 2% different from value at the room condition.

- ➤ **Design tip:** For commissioning purposes it is useful to know the required volume at the air outlets. In this example there is little difference between the two calculated volumes, but at higher temperature differentials the difference can be significant

- ➤ **Design tip:** The more the supply air mixes with room air before it enters the occupied zone, the higher the supply air/room air temperature differential that can be used. High ceiling diffusers that induce room air and use of the Coanda effect, such as diffusers/outlets that throw along a surface, can all allow more mixing.

- ➤ **Design tip:** If working in mass flow rate, it is advisable to check the volume flow rates (and *vice versa*).

Rules of thumb

- For general comfort applications air changes rates are unlikely to exceed 10 ach⁻¹, corresponding to a cooling temperature differential of 8-12 K.
- Guideline maximum supply temperature differentials for cooling are discussed in *CIBSE Guide B2*, Section 4.2.3.4:-

Application	Max temp differential K
High ceiling (large heat gains/low level input)	12
Low ceiling (air handling luminaires/low level input)	10
Low ceiling (downward discharge)	5

Source : Table 4.2 CIBSE Guide B2

References

CIBSE Guide B2, *Ventilation and Air Conditioning*, Section 3: Requirements – esp. Section 3.2.1 Indoor air quality requirements – offices, Section 3.2.2 Ventilation for internal comfort – offices, Section 4.2 Room air distribution. CIBSE 2001, ISBN 1 903287 16 2.

BSRIA, *Rules of Thumb*, TN 15/2001, BSRIA 2001, ISBN 086022 587 9

See also:

Sheet H6 Plant heating load
Sheet C3 Cooling plant load
Sheet C4 Ventilation – Fresh air requirements
Sheet C6 Heating/cooling coil sizing
Sheet A7 Grille and diffuser sizing

DESIGN WATCHPOINTS

1. Cooling supply air temperatures differentials tend to be more critical than heating as cold draughts cause more discomfort and cold air has negative buoyancy (cold air sinks).
2. Although cooling tends to be more critical, a high heating differential can also created problems as the air has positive buoyancy and will therefore tend to rise and stay at high level. A system that works well under cooling may therefore not give good air distribution under heating, so room air diffusion under both modes should always be considered.

C6 HEATING/ COOLING COIL SIZING

Overview

Air handling units use heating and cooling coils (also known as heating and cooling batteries) to heat and cool the air being used to supply the various spaces served by the plant.

These can use various energy sources including direct use of electricity, steam, or hot water from boiler plant for heating, and direct use of refrigerant via DX coils, chilled water or water/glycol mix from chiller plant for cooling. The required heating or cooling loads for the heating and cooling coils need to be known in order to specify and select appropriate equipment.

Heating coils

The air passing through a heating coil is heated sensibly, in other words the air temperature is increased and the moisture content remains unchanged.

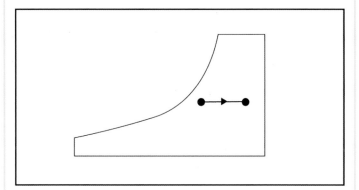

Cooling coils

The air passing through a cooling coil is first cooled sensibly, in that the air temperature is decreased and the moisture content remains unchanged. If the coil continues to cool the air to reach its dewpoint temperature then dehumidification will also occur as moisture condenses out of the air and the moisture content will reduce.

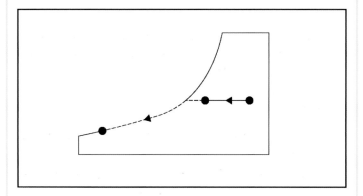

Design information required

Room internal design condition

The room internal design condition (air temperature, and moisture content or percentage saturation) is required as this is the condition that must be met by the design heating/cooling system.

External design condition

The external design condition (air temperature, and moisture content or percentage saturation) is required to give the air condition for outside air entering the plant.

Space heating and cooling loads

The heating and cooling loads (sensible and latent) for the various spaces served by the system are required in order to determine supply conditions.

Water flow and return temperatures (indirect coils)

The temperatures of the heating and cooling media are required for coil sizing for indirect coils.

Key design inputs

- Room air design condition for both summer and winter, both dry bulb air temperature t_a (°C) and moisture content g (kg/kg)
- Heating and cooling loads for the space (kW)
- Fresh air requirements (l/s) – Fresh air ventilation requirements for occupants or processes
- Fan gains – details of any fan gains ie temperature rise across fan

Design outputs

- Supply air condition under both heating and cooling: dry bulb air temperature t_a (°C) and moisture content g (kg/kg)
- Total mass flow rate of supply air (kg/s)
- Heating and cooling duties (kW)

Design approach

See also C5 – Supply air quantity and condition.

The supply air quantity and condition may have already been determined, but often this is done in combination with sizing of the required heating and cooling batteries and other plant.

The heating or cooling battery will have to meet both the room heating or cooling load, and the load imposed on the plant by any fresh air requirement. In the example below for heating only, the heating coil will have to meet both the sensible heating load for the space and the heating requirement to raise the fresh air component from outside air temperature to room temperature.

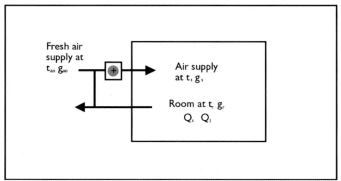

C6 HEATING/COOLING COIL SIZING

Calculation approach – heating coil

See also C5 – Supply air quantity and condition.

Step 1. Establish or calculate the required supply air mass flow rate and condition for both summer and winter cases (See C5 – Supply air quantity and condition). Decide whether a full fresh air system or one with re-circulation is required. (Check with senior engineer as required)

Step 2. Calculate required heating coil duty Q_h

   a. For full fresh air this is simply,

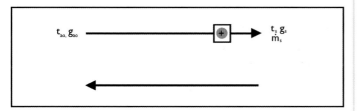

$$Q_h = \dot{m}_s \, c_p \, \Delta t$$

Where $\Delta t = (t_s - t_{ao})$, in other words all the supply air must be raised from the outside air temperature to the supply temperature.

   b. For recirculation this is,

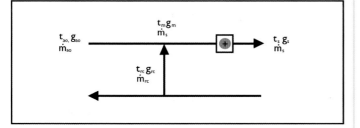

$$Q_h = \dot{m}_s \, c_p \, \Delta t$$

Where $\Delta t = (t_s - t_m)$, in other words all the supply air must be raised from the mix condition to the supply temperature.

This calculation can be done in several ways:

The mix condition can be calculated

Alternatively, thinking about what happens, the recirculated component must be raised from extract condition (often taken as the same as room condition) to supply condition and the outside air component must be raised from outside air temperature to the supply condition.

Step 3. For water to air heating coils calculate the mass flow rate(m_w) for flow and return from boiler circuit using

$$Q_h = \dot{m}_w \, c_p \, \Delta t$$

Where $\Delta t = (t_f - t_r)$ ie the difference between boiler flow and return temperatures.

(See heating and cooling Design Watchpoints on page 54)

Design tip:

> ➢ Often volume flow-rates are used, for example for fresh air ventilation requirements. These must be converted to mass flow rates using appropriate values of density or humid volume.

Example 1

Determine the supply air volume and temperature required for a warm air heating system for the following open plan office for:

* A full fresh air system and
* a recirculation system.

Design data
Winter design fabric heat loss is 12 kW
Internal design air temperature is 19°C
External design air temperature is −1°C
Occupancy minimum fresh air requirement is 250 l/s

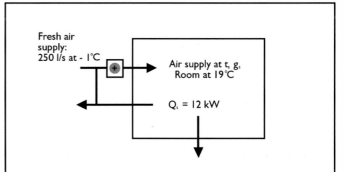

Step 1. Supply air temperature and volume - If the fresh air requirement only were used for heating:

$$\mathbf{250 \ l/s = 0.25 \ m^3/s}$$

$$Q_s = \dot{m}_s \, c_p \, \Delta t, \text{ where } \Delta t = (t_s - t_{ao})$$
$$= \dot{V} \rho \, c_p \, \Delta t$$

Humid volume at 19°C and say 50% saturation is 0.8365 m^3/kg, density is 1.195 kg/m^3 (data may be obtained from tables in *CIBSE Guide C*).

$$12 = 0.25 \times 1.195 \times 1.026 \times \Delta t$$
$$\Delta t = 39°C$$

This would give a supply air temperature of 58°C, which is high and obviously unacceptable.

Assuming a ceiling distribution for an average height office, an acceptable Δt for heating would probably be around 8–12°C, depending on throw. Selecting a Δt of 10°C, giving a supply air temperature of 29°C

$$Q = \dot{m}_s \, c_p \, \Delta t$$
$$12 = \dot{m}_s \times 1.026 \times 10$$
$$\dot{m}_s = 1.17 \text{ kg/s}$$
$$\dot{V} = m/\rho = 1.17/1.195 = 0.98 m^3/s$$

In other words a supply volume flow rate of, say, 1 m^3/s at 29°C

© BSRIA BG 30/2003

C6 HEATING/COOLING COIL SIZING

Step 2. Heating coil size for full fresh air

$$Q_h = \dot{m}_s\, c_p\, \Delta t$$

Where

$\Delta t = (t_s - t_{ao})$
$Q_h = 1\cdot17 \times 1\cdot026 \times (29 + 1)$
$\quad = 36\ kW$

Heating coil size for recirculation (method 1)

$Q_h = \dot{m}_s\, c_p\, \Delta t$
$\quad = 0\cdot25 \times 1\cdot195 \times 1\cdot026 \times (29 + 1)$ (fresh air component)
$\quad + 0\cdot73 \times 1\cdot195 \times 1\cdot026 \times (29-19)$ (recirculated component)
$\quad = 9\cdot2 + 8\cdot9 = 18\cdot1\ kW$

Heating coil size for recirculation (method 2)

By thinking about what happens, the heating coil load under recirculation can also be worked out as the heat to raise the fresh air component up to room temperature so it is neutral plus the sensible heat load for the space:

$(0\cdot25 \times 1\cdot195 \times 1\cdot026 \times (19 + 1)\,) + 12$
$= 6\cdot1 + 12$
$= 18\cdot1\ kW$

Heating coil size for recirculation (method 3)

A third approach is to find the mix condition and then look at the load across the coil:

$\dot{m}_s \times t_m = \dot{m}_{rc} \times t_{rc} + \dot{m}_{ao} \times t_{ao}$
$1\cdot17 \times t_m = (0\cdot73 \times 1\cdot195 \times 19) + (0\cdot25 \times 1\cdot195 \times -1)$
$\qquad = 16\cdot28$
$t_m = 13\cdot9°C$
$Q_h = \dot{m}_s\, c_p\, \Delta t$
$\quad = 1\cdot17 \times 1\cdot026 \times (29-13\cdot9)$
$\quad = 18\cdot1\ kW$

Assumptions
- Return air is the same temperature as the room air
- Air density is the same throughout the system – an average value was used throughout at the room condition. In practice it changes with temperature
- Fan and duct gains have been ignored

Step 3. Calculate the required mass flow rates of hot water for an indirect heating coil.

Assume flow and return hot water temperatures of 80°C and 70°C:

$$Q_h = \dot{m}_w\, c_p\, \Delta t$$

Where:
$\Delta t = (t_f - t_r)$
$18\cdot1 = \dot{m}_w \times 4\cdot2 \times 10$
$\dot{m}_w = 0\cdot43\ kg/s$

Calculation approach – cooling coil
See also C5 – Supply air quantity and condition.
See also calculation approach – heating coil.

Step 1. Establish/calculate required supply air mass flow rate and condition for both summer and winter cases. (See C5 – Supply air quantity and condition.) Decide whether a full fresh air system or one with re-circulation is required. (Check with senior engineer as required.)

Step 2. Calculate required cooling coil duty Q_c.
a) For sensible cooling, at constant moisture content. In other words with $g_a = g_s$, all parts of the cooling coil in contact with the air stream must be above the dewpoint temperature of the entering air stream.

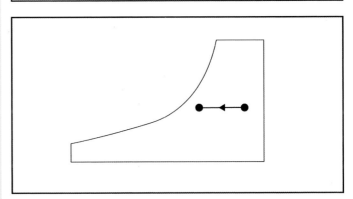

The cooling coil load is given by:
$$Q_c = \dot{m}_s\, c_p\, \Delta t$$

Where:
$\Delta t = (t_a - t_s)$,

Alternatively:
$$Q_c = \dot{m}_s\, \Delta h$$

Where Δh = the specific enthalpy (kJ/kg) difference between the on coil and off coil conditions:
ie $(h_a - h_s)$,

b) For sensible cooling with dehumidification

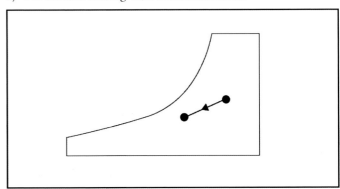

$Q_c = \dot{m}_s\, \Delta h$

C6 HEATING/COOLING COIL SIZING

Where Δh = the specific enthalpy (kJ/kg) difference between the on coil and off coil conditions:

$$(h_a - h_s)$$

For a full fresh air system the on coil condition (t_a, h_a) will be the outside design condition.

For a system with recirculation the on coil condition will be the mix condition. The mix condition can be found using the same procedure shown in the heating coil sizing procedure and example ie:

$$\dot{m}_s \times t_m = \dot{m}_{rc} \times t_{rc} + \dot{m}_{ao} \times t_{ao}$$

The moisture content of the mix condition can be found in the same way:

$$\dot{m}_s \times g_m = \dot{m}_{rc} \times g_{rc} + \dot{m}_{ao} \times g_{ao}$$

Step 3. For indirect cooling coils calculate the mass flow rate (m_w) for flow and return from chiller circuit using

$$Q_c = \dot{m}_w\, c_p\, \Delta t$$

Where:

$\Delta t = (t_r - t_f)$ ie the difference between chiller flow and return temperatures.

Example 2

Determine the supply air volume and temperature required and the cooling coil load for summer operation for the following space.

Design data
Summer sensible heat gain is 10 kW.
Latent heat gain is 3 kW.
Internal design air condition is 20°C, 50% sat.
Summer external design air condition is 28°C, 50% sat.

Occupancy minimum fresh air requirement is 325 l/s.
Acceptable supply temperature in summer is 14°C.

Step 1. Supply air volume and temperature - considering the cooling case first.

$$Q_s = \dot{m}_s\, c_p\, \Delta t$$
$$10 = \dot{m}_s \times 1 \cdot 026 \times (20{-}14)$$
$$\dot{m}_s = 1 \cdot 626 \text{ kg/s}$$

The latent gain is given by:

$$Q_l = \dot{m}\, h_{fg}\, \Delta g$$
$$3 = 1 \cdot 626 \times 2450 \times \Delta g$$
$$\Delta g = (g_r - g_s) = 0 \cdot 000753 \text{ kg/kg}$$

From psychrometric data the space moisture content g_r is $0 \cdot 00738$ kg/kg. The supply air moisture content g_s is given by:

$$g_s = 0 \cdot 00738 - 0 \cdot 000753 = 0 \cdot 00663 \text{ kg/kg}$$

The summer supply condition is therefore $1 \cdot 626$ kg/s at 14°C and a g of $0 \cdot 00663$ kg/kg.

The humid volume at this condition is $0 \cdot 8218$ m^3/kg, so the required volume flow rate is:

$$\dot{V} = \dot{m} \times v = 1 \cdot 626 \times 0 \cdot 8218$$
$$= 1 \cdot 336 \text{ m}^3/\text{s}$$

Considering the minimum fresh air requirement of 325 l/s this gives a value of 25% fresh air and 75% recirculated.

Step 2. Coil capacity - A mix condition can now be found and the cooling coil sized.

$$\dot{m}_s \times t_m = \dot{m}_{rc} \times t_{rc} + \dot{m}_{ao} \times t_{ao}$$
$$1 \cdot 626 \times t_m = (0 \cdot 75 \times 1 \cdot 626 \times 20) + (0 \cdot 25 \times 1 \cdot 626 \times 28)$$
$$t_m = 22°C$$

> **Design tip:** Thinking about the mix temperature will tell you that the mix point is 75% of the way between 28 and 20 which gives the answer instantly.

$$\dot{m}_s \times g_m = \dot{m}_{rc} \times g_{rc} + \dot{m}_{ao} \times g_{ao}$$
$$1 \cdot 626 \times g_m = (0 \cdot 75 \times 1 \cdot 626 \times 0 \cdot 00738) + (0 \cdot 25 \times 1 \cdot 626 \times 0 \cdot 01210).$$
$$g_m = 0 \cdot 00856 \text{ kg/kg}$$
$$Q = \dot{m}_s\, \Delta h = (h_a - h_m)$$

From psychromatic data, using t and g
Enthalpy at mix condition is $43 \cdot 88$ kJ/kg
Enthalpy at supply condition is $30 \cdot 83$ kJ/kg

$$Q_c = 1 \cdot 626 \times (43 \cdot 88 - 30 \cdot 83)$$
$$= 21 \cdot 22 \text{ kW}$$

Alternatively, as it is enthalpies that are used to size the coil, then a mix enthalpy condition can be found initially using the enthalpies of the two air streams.

Step 3. Cooling medium mass flow rate - Calculate the required mass flow rates of chilled water for water to air heating coil.

Assume flow and return chilled water temperatures of 6 and 12°C
$$Q_c = \dot{m}_w\, c_p\, \Delta t$$

Where $\Delta t = (t_f - t_r)$
$$21 \cdot 22 = \dot{m}_w \times 4 \cdot 2 \times 6$$
$$\dot{m}_w = 0 \cdot 84 \text{ kg/s}$$

Assumptions applying to example 2
- Return air is the same temperature as the room air
- Fan and duct gains have been ignored
- Coil contact factors have not been included in this simple example
- The adp (apparatus dew point) of the coil has also not been considered. In practice a coil will cool down a line on the psychrometric chart from the mix point to the adp, which provides dehumidification. This can over-cool the air and thus necessitate reheat to achieve the required supply temperature.

C6 HEATING/COOLING COIL SIZING

References

CIBSE Guide B2, *Ventilation and Air Conditioning*, Section 3: requirements – esp. Section 3.2.1 Indoor air quality requirements – offices, Section 3.2.2 Ventilation for internal comfort – offices, Section 4 Systems, CIBSE 2001, ISBN 1 903287 16 2.

CIBSE Guide C, *Reference Data*, 2001, ISBN 7506 5360 4

Lawrence Race G, *Design Checks for HVAC – A Quality Control Framework for Building Services Engineers* – Sheet 50, Air handling units, AG 1/2002, BSRIA 2002, ISBN 0 86022 589 5

BSRIA, *Rules of Thumb*, TN 15/2001, BSRIA 2001, ISBN 086022 587 9

There are many text books available that provide further data on psychrometrics and the design of air conditioning systems eg:

Jones WP, *Air Conditioning Engineering,* 5th edition, 2001, ISBN 075 065 0745
Legg R, *Air Conditioning Systems Design, Comissioning and Maintenance*, 1991, ISBN 0 7134 5644 2

See also:

Sheet H6 Plant heating load
Sheet C3 Cooling plant load
Sheet C4 Ventilation – Fresh air requirements
Sheet C5 Supply air quantity and condition

DESIGN WATCHPOINTS

1. The basic heat transfer equation $Q = m\, c_p\, \Delta t$ is used many times. Always stop and think what fluid it applies to (air or water or water/glycol mix) and what temperature difference is correct. Ensure the correct value for specific heat capacity is used.
2. Return air can be at a different temperature to the room air condition. With high level extract or extract via air-handling luminaries, it may well be 1-2°C above the room condition which can impose an additional load on a cooling coil.
3. Dehumidification requirements can sometimes necessitate a larger cooling coil than would be required for sensible cooling only.
4. Air density will vary throughout a system.
5. Fan and duct gains can add an additional heat gain to a system that can impose an additional load on a cooling coil.
6. Apply any correction necessary for density of air due to the altitude of the site. An incorrect value used in the calculations could result in the plant being undersized.
7. Coils using refrigerant (direct expansion) as the cooling medium are more complicated.
8. Heating coils using steam, refrigerant (in a heat pump) or directly fired coils are more complicated.

C7 HUMIDIFIER DUTY

Overview

During winter, the air intake to an air conditioning system may be too dry for comfort conditions in the supplied space. For this reason humidifiers often form part of the air-handling unit to add moisture to the air before being delivered to the space.

The air can be humidified in two ways. The most common is with steam humidification. The water is already converted to vapour or steam before entering the supply airflow.

The second method is adiabatic humidification. Humidification is achieved by adding droplets (or a spray) of water to the airflow. When spraying water into the airflow it is important to consider the potential risks associated with humidifier fever and Legionnaires' Disease, (see CIBSE, *Technical Memorandum TM13, Minimising the risk of Legionnaires' disease, 2002*).

A psychrometric chart or data is needed in order to calculate the humidifier duty.

Design information required

Design conditions

Agreed outside conditions for winter and summer, internal conditions, and design supply air conditions.

Type of humidifier

Steam or adiabatic, steam humidification is the last process in air conditioning before the air is delivered to the space. With adiabatic humidification, the air is re-heated after humidification.

Mass flow rate of air

The mass flow rate should already be known, but if not, it can be determined from the air volume flow rate and density

Steam humidification

Direct steam injection

Steam is provided from either a boiler or from a local steam generator (humidifier). Steam humidification provides the following:

- No latent heat for evaporation – this is added before the steam enters the air stream
- There is an increase in the enthalpy of the air and moisture content.

Isothermal process

The dry bulb temperature of the air remains almost constant and may be referred to as isothermal.

The load on the humidifier is given by:

$$Q_h = \dot{m}_a (h_b - h_a)$$

The mass flow rate of the steam supplied is given by:

$$\dot{m}_s = \dot{m}_a (g_b - g_a)$$

Where:

Q_h = humidifier load,

$\dot{m}_a$ = mass flow rate of air,

h_a = enthalpy at point A,

h_b = enthalpy at point B,

g_a = moisture content at point A,

g_b = moisture content at point B,

t_s = supply air temperature,

$\dot{m}_s$ = mass flow rate of steam.

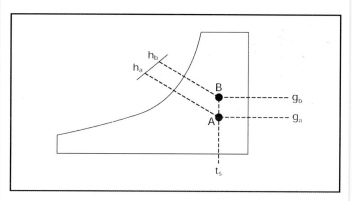

It is assumed that the process is isothermal and therefore the dry bulb temperature remains constant.

Example 1

Calculate the humidifier duty and quantity of steam supplied using the following data:

$\dot{m}_a$ = 1·4 kg/s,

g_a = 0·004 kg/kg,

g_b = 0·008 kg/kg,

h_a = 25·18 kJ/kg,

h_b = 35·30 kJ/kg,

Therefore:

$$Q_h = 1·4 (35·3 - 25·18) = 14·168 kW$$
$$\dot{m}_s = 1·4 (0·008 - 0·004) = 0·0056 \text{ kg/s}$$

© BSRIA BG 30/2003

C7 HUMIDIFIER DUTY

Adiabatic humidification

This type of humidifier sprays water directly into the air stream. The water may be introduced either by a spinning disc or by a pressurised water nozzle or by ultra-sonics. Water that is not evaporated into the air stream will either be drained away or recycled back into the air stream.

Although adiabatic humidifiers are a simple method of introducing moisture to air, they need to be checked and maintained regularly as there is a risk of Legionella and other contaminants developing. This risk is increased if some non-evaporated water is then recycled and not treated correctly.

Adiabatic humidification provides the following:

Constant enthalpy: ($h_a = h_b$), the enthalpy difference is negligible to the extent that the effectiveness of the humidification process is expressed in terms of moisture content.

Reduced dry bulb temperature: the water vapour that enters the air picks up the latent heat of evaporation from the air, which causes the dry bulb temperature to reduce. Because of this a re-heat battery is often used.

The adiabatic humidifier is defined in terms of the mass flow rate of water to the humidifier (m_w). This will vary with the efficiency of the process in which the water is delivered.

$$\text{Eff} = \frac{\dot{m}_w}{\dot{m}_a \left(g_b - g_a \right)}$$

Note: $\dot{m}_s = \dot{m}_a \left(g_b - g_a \right)$

The process is shown on the chart below.

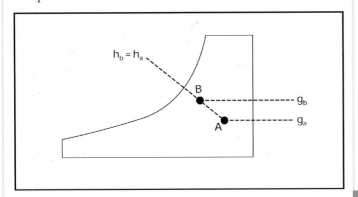

Example 2

For the following values, calculate the quantity of water supplied.

Where:

$\dot{m}_a = 1 \cdot 5$ kg/s,

$g_a = 0 \cdot 005$ kg/kg,

$g_b = 0 \cdot 009$ kg/kg,

eff $= 60\%$

Then:

$$60 = \frac{\dot{m}_w}{1 \cdot 5(0 \cdot 009 - 0 \cdot 005)} \times 100$$

$$\dot{m}_w = 60 \times 1 \cdot 5 \times 0 \cdot 004 \div 100 = 0 \cdot 0036 \text{ kg/s}$$

References:

CIBSE, *Minimising the Risk of Legionnaires' Disease,* Technical Memorandum TM13, 2002, ISBN 190328 723 5.

See also

Sheet C5 Supply air quantity and condition
Sheet C6 Heating/cooling coil sizing

Lawrence Race G, *Design Checks for HVAC – A Quality Control Framework for Building Services Engineers* – sheet 51, AG 1/2002, BSRIA 2001, ISBN 0 86022 589 5

DESIGN WATCHPOINTS

1. Steam humidification normally requires large energy use (invariably electrical) which can be easily forgotten in building energy predictions.
2. Ensure that the electrical loads for humidification are included in the electrical distribution schematic for the overall design. These loads may be considerable.
3. Steam humidifiers are often high maintenance items and may require treated water supplies.
4. There are various ways of determining humidifier efficiency, consult your senior engineer.

The following section contains six building services engineering topic areas related to the design of water flow distribution systems.

The following two pages contain flow charts of the relevant design and calculation processes.

The first flow chart shows the six topics within this section.

The second flow chart provides an overview of the process, showing some of the many related topics that need to be considered in the design of water flow distribution systems. The boxes highlighted in blue show an area that is fully or partially covered within one of the six topic areas in this section, or in the rest of the guidance, with the appropriate reference numbers given.

FLOW CHART 1 – TOPICS WITHIN THIS SECTION

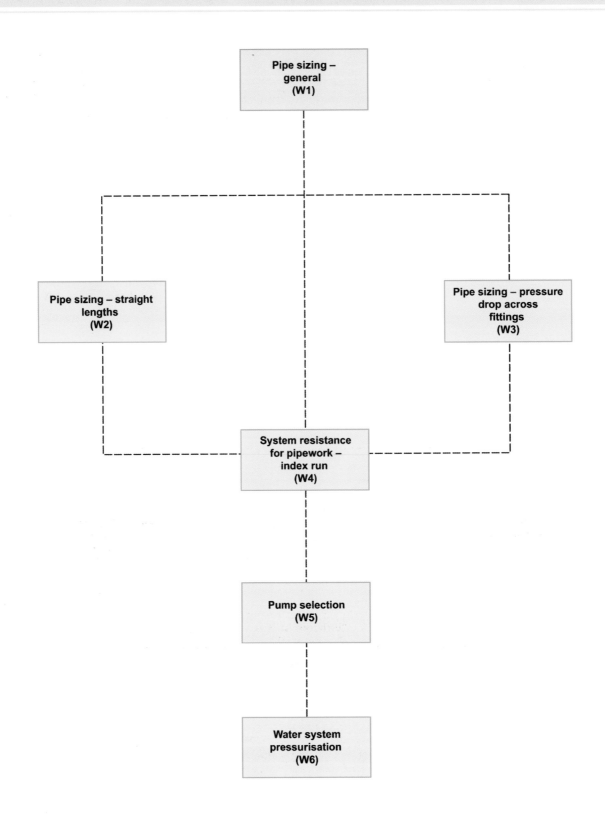

FLOW CHART 2 – OVERVIEW OF SYSTEM DESIGN PROCESS

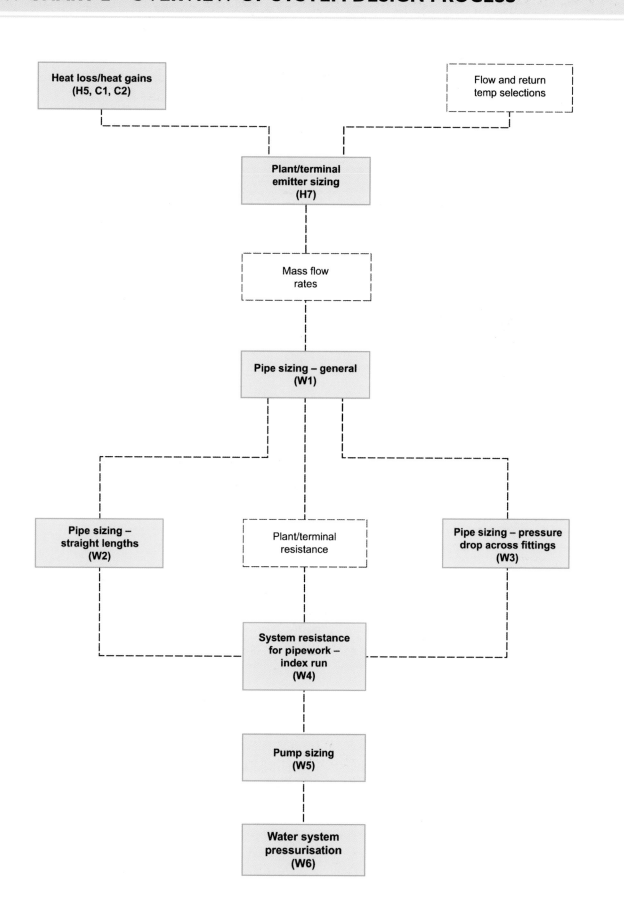

This chart shows the design areas relevant to this design process. Where design areas are wholly or partially discussed in this document the relevant sheet references are given in brackets

© BSRIA BG 30/2003

W1 PIPE SIZING - GENERAL

Overview

Whenever a fluid flows along a pipe, there will be a loss of pressure due to friction. This pressure drop depends, among other factors, on the fluid velocity. So, for a required fluid flow rate, the pipe diameter and pressure loss are related. A small diameter pipe will result in high fluid velocity and so a high pressure loss; a larger pipe carrying the same flow rate will result in a lower velocity and pressure loss. Pipe sizing involves determining the most appropriate pipe diameters to use and the resulting velocities and pressure losses.

There are limits to acceptable fluid velocity. High velocities lead to noise and erosion while low velocity can give problems with air-locking (*CIBSE Guide C*, Table 4.4). While pipe capital costs are obviously related to diameter, the running costs for pumped systems, are proportional to pressure loss. Therefore, pipe sizing involves value engineering.

With gravity systems, (for example cold water down services), the available head is the limiting factor. Pipe sizing involves determining the pipe sizes which will deliver the design flow rate at a total pressure loss equal to this head.

Pressure loss is found to be proportional to velocity pressure:

$$\Delta P \propto \frac{1}{2}\rho v^2$$

For practical purposes, the pressure losses through straight pipes and pipe fittings are dealt with separately.

Straight pipes

The equation above is written as:

$$\Delta P = \frac{\lambda L}{d} \times \frac{1}{2}\rho v^2$$

(Known as the D'Arcy Equation)

Where:

 Δ = pressure loss (Pa)
 ρ = density of the fluid (kg/m^3)
 λ = friction factor
 l = length of pipe (m)
 v = mean velocity of water flow (m/s)
 d = internal pipe diameter (m)

This equation can be solved mathematically. However, λ is not easily determined as it is related to the Reynolds number and the relative roughness of the pipe wall. Therefore in practice, pipe sizing is usually carried out using data already calculated for certain commonly used pipe materials and flow temperatures such as that given in the pipe sizing tables in *CIBSE Guide C* Section 4. For example, tables C4.9-C4.33 in *CIBSE Guide C*, provide data on the flow of water in straight pipes of various materials, including copper, UPVC and steel at two temperatures: 10°C and 75°C.

(See sheet W2 Pipe sizing – straight lengths for a worked example.)

(See Design Watchpoint 1.)

Pipe fittings

In this case the above equation is written as:

$$\Delta P = \zeta \times \frac{1}{2}\rho v^2$$

Where ζ is the coefficient of velocity pressure loss. Values of ζ are found from tables in Section 4 of *CIBSE Guide C*. Alternatively, the concept of equivalent length can be used, values of which are given in the tables for straight pipes.

(See sheet W3 Pipe sizing – fittings for a worked example.)

Pipe sizes

Standard pipe sizes quoted are nominal and are not the internal diameter. In *CIBSE Guide C* internal diameters are listed in tables 4.2 or 4.3.

Fluids other than water

The tables in *CIBSE Guide C* are for water only. For other fluids (such as oil, brine) the D'Arcy equation should be used. For compressible fluids (for example steam, compressed air and natural gas), the equations above are not applicable and reference should be made to the specialised pipe sizing tables in the *CIBSE Guide C*.

Pipe sizing can be carried out either manually or using a spreadsheet or computer-based sizing package. However, in all cases, correct input data must be used and output cross-checked.

Further information is available in *CIBSE Guide C*, and *CIBSE Guide B1*.

➤ **Design tip:** Ducts are sized using the same principles. For practical purposes, charts rather than tables are used for straight ducts. (See sheet A1 Duct Sizing.)

Design information required

Type of system supplied

For example radiators and cooling coils and batteries. This will determine what is acceptable in terms of flow temperatures, pressure drops and noise. Consult a senior engineer as necessary.

Details of fluid

For example water, gas and glycol solution.

This will enable fluid properties to be determined such as fluid density and viscosity.

➤ **Design tip:** If the system fluid is chilled water containing glycol, then the specific heat capacity will need to be adjusted.

Fluid temperature

For example whether hot or chilled water. Typical flow temperatures for low temperature hot water systems are 70-95°C, and for primary chilled water are 6-12°C.

Design flow and return temperatures

To give the temperature drop across system. This will be needed to determine the required mass flow rate.

© BSRIA BG 30/2003

W1 PIPE SIZING – GENERAL

> **Design tip**: Do not assume that 82/71°C must be used for low temperature hot water systems. Doubling the temperature drop will have a relatively small effect on the heating surface required but will reduce the flow rate required by half, therefore the pipe sizes and the pump duty will be smaller. The control of the heat output will also be improved.

Pipe material
For example copper, steel etc. This determines pipe roughness and hence the flow characteristics and pipe pressure losses.

Pipe insulation details
Whether pipes are insulated and, if so, insulation details – this governs losses from the pipes and the extra heating or cooling required to compensate for this.

Pipe system layout
Including pipe lengths, number and type of fittings etc.

Distribution space available
Horizontally and vertically such as false ceiling depths and risers.

Details of ambient conditions
Surrounding air temperature and whether the pipes will have to run through chilled or outdoor spaces.

Key design inputs
- Design mass flow rates in kg/s
- Limiting maximum pipe pressure loss per metre run in Pa/m
- Limiting maximum and minimum flow velocity in metres per second

> **Design tip:** A minimum velocity may also be set to avoid scale settling etc.

Design outputs
- Schematic of pipework layout and associated plant showing required flow rates
- Schedule of pipe sizes and lengths, and fittings such as elbows and valves

Design approach
Pipe sizing should ensure that both pressure drop and velocity are acceptable to ensure efficient operation. Pipe diameter is therefore often selected on a pre-determined pressure drop per unit length or a pre-determined velocity. The design criteria may require a system that is designed with a pre-selected pressure drop but also operates within a maximum velocity limit. Note the following:

1. Design should minimise pipe and valve noise, erosion, installation and operating costs.
2. Small pipe sizes can result in high flow velocities, noise, erosion, and high pumping costs.
3. Large pipe sizes will increase installation costs and make it difficult to vent air.

Rule of thumb design data
Water flow temperature – heating
LTHW: 70-95°C
MTHW: 100-120°C
HTHW: over 120°C
(Above 95°C the system should be pressurised to avoid the risk of flash steam formation.)

Water flow temperatures – chilled water
Chilled water primary circuits flow temperatures: 6-12°C
Chilled water secondary circuits flow temperatures: 10-15°C

Water velocities
Steel pipe up to 50 mm diameter: 0·75-1·5 m/s
Steel pipe over 50 mm diameter: 1·25-3 m/s
Small bore systems: <1 m/s
Microbore systems: 1·2 m/s
Corrosive water systems: 2m/s maximum.

Pressure drop
Typical range for re-circulating system pipe sizes over 50 mm is 100-300 Pa/m. For under 50 mm a similar range may be used but it is essential to check that the velocity is acceptable. *CIBSE Guide C*, suggests a suitable starting point of 250 Pa/m.

Further information is available in *CIBSE Guide C*, section 4 and *CIBSE Guide B1*, Section 5.1.3 and appendix A1.3.

References
CIBSE Guide B1, *Heating*, Section 5.1.3 and appendix A1.3, 2002, ISBN 19032 8720 0
CIBSE Guide C, *Reference Data*, Section 4, 2001, ISBN 7506 5360 4
BSRIA, *Rules of Thumb*, TN 15/2001, BSRIA 2001, ISBN 086022 587 9
Lawrence Race G, *Design Checks for HVAC – A Quality Control Framework for Building Services Engineers* – sheets 26 and 44, AG 1/2002, BSRIA 2002, ISBN 0 86022 589 5

See also:
Sheet W2 Pipe sizing - Straight lengths
Sheet W3 Pipe sizing - Pressure drop across fittings
Sheet W4 System resistance for pipework - Index run

DESIGN WATCHPOINTS

1. If pipe materials or flow temperatures differ markedly from the standard tables then pipe sizing should be done using initial fluid flow equations with appropriate data. Otherwise errors could occur, resulting in incorrectly sized pumps and inadequate heat delivery.
2. Check that both flow velocities and pressure drops are within acceptable limits.
3. Check pipes and fittings can withstand maximum system working pressure.
4. Check that all of the system operates under positive static pressure to ensure any leaks are obvious and air does not enter system.
5. Pipework systems can suffer from a number of problems that must be considered during design – including:
   - dirt blockages
   - air locking
   - erosion - due to cavitation effect and the scouring effect of dirt particles
   - corrosion - if system materials and water quality are not carefully considered.

© BSRIA BG 30/2003

W2 PIPE SIZING – STRAIGHT LENGTHS

Overview

In order to size pipework both straight lengths and fittings need to be considered. Initial pipe sizing is done by considering straight runs alone, but for complete system design and pump sizing both straight runs and fittings need to be considered.

The examples in the pipe sizing, index run and pump sizing sheets (W2-5) are shown as manual calculations. Although calculations are often done on a spreadsheet or by using a computer sizing package, these will still require input and design decisions that require familiarity with the fundamental theory and manual sizing procedures.

Design information required

Pipe length in metres

This may already have been provided on schematics.

(See also sheet W1.)
(See Design Watchpoint 1.)

Fluid type and operating temperature

The specific heat capacity, density and viscosity of fluids will depend on the type used. (Properties of various fluids are given in *CIBSE Guide C* Appendix 4.A1.)

Temperature drop across system (K)

Δt across the system.

Pipe material

Calculation procedure (manual pipe sizing)

Step 1. If not already laid out, sketch the system under consideration, indicating pipe lengths and unit loads (kW). Allocate a reference number to each length of pipework.

Step 2. Estimate the pipe emission for each section (often taken as a percentage of unit load such as 5-10%, or as a typical value such as 25 W/m run for insulated heating pipes, 100 W/m run for un-insulated pipes) to give the total load for each section. The pipe emission will depend on pipe orientation (vertical/horizontal) and the quality and installation of insulation. Emissions can be less than 5% if the pipes are well insulated.

> **Design tip:** Typical values can be obtained by estimating the pipe size and reviewing pipe emission data in tables 3.17 - 3.20 of *CIBSE Guide C*.

Step 3. Select an appropriate temperature drop across the system, such as 10-20 K for low pressure hot water and, assuming this to be constant across the system, calculate the mass flow rate in each section.

Step 4. Select an acceptable design value for either pressure drop per unit length or velocity. (See sheet W1 and seek advice from senior engineer as required.)

Step 5. Size pipe using tables 4.9-4.33 of the *CIBSE Guide C*. Select an appropriate pipe size using the mass flow rate and the selected value of either pressure drop per metre run or velocity.

Step 6. Note the equivalent length factor (l_e) for the pipe section from the table as this will be used to establish pressure drops through fittings. (See W3 - Pipe fittings guidance.)

l_e = equivalent length of pipe, in other words the length for a pressure drop equal to velocity pressure.

> **Design tip:** Pipe sizing and pressure loss data for a system can be laid out in a tabular format and converted to a spreadsheet.

Example

Find the pipe size for a 10 m straight run of medium steel heating pipe carrying water at 75°C and serving four fan convectors, each rated at 4·15 kW output.

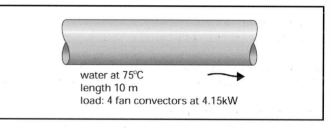

water at 75°C
length 10 m
load: 4 fan convectors at 4.15kW

Step 1. A simple sketch above shows the necessary information

Step 2. Estimate the pipe emission with an assumed estimated loss as 6% of the load.

Hence:
    Total fan coil load = 4 x 4·15 = 16·6 kW,
    6% of 16·6 = 0·996 kW
    Total load = 17·6 kW

Step 3. Temperature drop across system assumed as 10K, from
$Q = \dot{m} \times Cp \times \Delta t$

Where:
    Q = load (kW)
    Cp = specific heat capacity of water (kJ/kg.K)
    Δt = temperature difference (K)

Mass flow rate is therefore:
$$\dot{m} = \frac{17 \cdot 6}{4 \cdot 2 \times 10} = 0 \cdot 42 \text{ kg/s}$$

Step 4. A pressure drop per metre run of 250 Pa/m is selected

Step 5. Using *CIBSE Guide* table 4.11 for medium grade steel pipe with water at 75°C, size the pipe to give the required mass flow rate and pressure drop per metre run. From the table it can be found that for a 25 mm diameter pipe, a mass flow rate of 0·411 kg/s gives a pressure drop of 240 Pa/m, and a mass flowrate of 0·428 kg/s gives a pressure drop of 260 Pa/m. By interpolating the mass flow rate to 0·42kg/s the pressure drop is found to be 250·58 Pa/m run with a velocity of approximately 0·75 m/s.

Cross-check: a velocity of 0·75 m/s is acceptable for 25 mm steel pipe

W2 PIPE SIZING – STRAIGHT LENGTHS

Step 6. The equivalent length factor is 1·1.

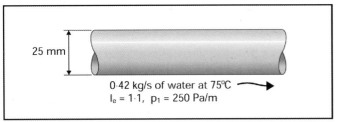

25 mm

0·42 kg/s of water at 75°C →
$l_e = 1·1$, $p_1 = 250$ Pa/m

Note that as an alternative approach to step 2, an experienced estimate of pipe size of 25 mm gives a pipe emission for steel pipe of 92 W/m run (*CIBSE Guide C*, table 3.17), in other words 920 W. This is 5·55 % of the total load, therefore the original assumed loss of 6% is reasonable.

➤ **Design tip:** Review the impact of a change of temperature drop across the system. Larger temperature drops (20K is common in Europe) can reduce pipe sizes considerably, but this will re quire more careful balancing of the system when commissioning.

➤ **Design tip:** For occupied spaces consider omitting pipe emission from radiator sizes. Any emission from the pipes to the occupied space is useful heating. As long as the total design capacity is available, it does not matter that some comes from the pipes and some from the emitters. This will also reduce pipe size, and reduce unnecessary system over sizing

References

CIBSE Guide B1, *Heating*, Section 5.1.3, and appendix A1.3, 2002, ISBN 19032 8720 0
CIBSE Guide C, *Reference Data*, Section 4, 2001, ISBN 7506 5360 4
BSRIA, *Rules of Thumb*, TN 15/2001, BSRIA 2001, ISBN 086022 587 9
Lawrence Race G, *Design Checks for HVAC – A Quality Control Framework for Building Services Engineers* – sheets 26 and 4, AG 1/2002, BSRIA 2002, ISBN 0 86022 589 5

See also:

Sheet W1 Pipe sizing – General
Sheet W3 Pipe sizing – Pressure drop across fittings
Sheet W4 System resistance for pipework – Index run

DESIGN WATCHPOINTS

1. If taking dimensions from drawings use dime nsions shown rather than scaling off, as drawings can become distorted if photocopied.
2. If pressure drop was selected, check that the velocity falls within a reasonable range and vice versa.
3. The pipe sizing tables in Guide C for heating systems have been calculated for fluid temperatures at 75 °C. Correction factors for fluid flows other than 75 °C are available in *CIBSE Guide B1* table 5.10. These factors are to be used with the equation 5.11 in *CIBSE Guide B1* (shown below), where C is the correction factor and ΔP_{75} is the tabulated pressure drop at 75°C.

    $$\Delta P = C \, \Delta P_{75}$$

    This correction factor may need to be individually applied to the pressure drops of flow and return pipe work. For example flow at 60°C will have a different correction factor depending on whether return temperature is 50°C or 40°C. This correction factor is required due to the change of viscosity of the fluid with temperature.

W3 PIPE SIZING – PRESSURE DROP ACROSS FITTINGS

Overview

There are two methods of calculating the total pressure loss through a fitting:

$$\Delta P = \zeta \times 0.5 \times \rho \times v^2 \text{ (CIBSE Guide C, equation 4·15)}$$

or

$$\Delta P = \zeta \times l_e \times \Delta P/l \text{ (CIBSE Guide C, equation 4·16)}$$

Where:

ΔP = total pressure loss (Pa),
ζ = pressure loss factor
ρ = density (kg/m^3)
v = velocity (m/s)
l_e = equivalent length of pipe, in other words the length for a pressure drop equal to velocity pressure
$\Delta P/l$ = pressure drop per unit length (per metre run)

Values of l_e and $\Delta P/l$ are given in the pipe sizing tables in *CIBSE Guide C*, section 4.

The ζ values represent the fraction of one velocity pressure that has the same pressure loss as the fitting.

The equivalent length of a pipe is that length which will produce a frictional pressure loss of one velocity pressure. l_e is equivalent length of pipe, (the length for a pressure drop equal to velocity pressure).

Design information required

(See also sheet W1 pipe sizing – general)

Pipe system layout

Pipe lengths, location, number and type of fittings,

Pipe sizes

When the straight length diameters have been calculated, the corresponding l_e and $\Delta P/l$ for each section may be required. When calculating the pressure drop across a branch fitting, the ζ for the straight section and branch section will be determined separately These will then be used to calculate the pressure drop across both parts of the branch.

Mass flow rate

The mass flow rate through each section and therefore through the fittings is required. Again, with a fitting such as a swept diverging tee, (such as a branch), the mass flow-rate at each part of the tee will be required. For example, one flow into the tee (1) and two flows out of the tee (2 and 3) as shown below:

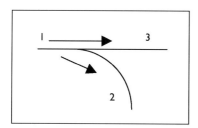

Calculation procedure

To calculate the pressure loss through a fitting the following steps are required:

Step 1. Find the appropriate velocity pressure loss factor (ζ) value for the fitting in tables 4.47-4.59 of *CIBSE Guide C*.

Step 2. Find the equivalent length (l_e) for the type/size of pipe to which the fitting will be connected (tables 4.9 to 4.33 *CIBSE Guide C*).

Step 3. Multiply the ζ value by the equivalent length to give the actual equivalent length of pipework which the fitting represents in terms of pressure loss.

Step 4. The equivalent length of pipe work can now be added to the actual pipe work in the system, thus enabling pipe work and fittings to be considered as a single entity (see example).

Example

Calculate the pressure loss through a 90° sharp elbow with a smooth radiused inner of 25 mm diameter connected to a medium grade steel pipe and passing a water flow rate of 0·5 kg/s at 75°C.

Step 1. From *CIBSE Guide C* table C4.48 (pressure loss factors for elbows) the ζ value for a 90° sharp elbow with a smooth radiused inner with a 25 mm diameter is 0·8

Step 2. From *CIBSE Guide C* table 4.11, details of the pipe associated with the elbow can be found. This is medium grade steel pipe with a 25 mm diameter carrying 0·5 kg/s of water at 75°C.

A flow rate of 0·493kg/s gives a pressure drop of 340 Pa/m.

A flow rate of 0·508kg/s gives a pressure drop of 360 Pa/m,

By interpolating to 0·5kg/s, a pressure drop of 349·33 Pa/m is found with an equivalent length factor of 1·1.

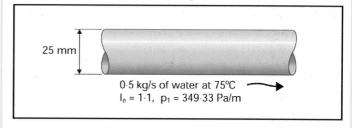

Step 3. The equivalent length of straight pipe represented by the fitting is $\zeta \times l_e = 0.8 \times 1.1 = 0.88$ m.

© BSRIA BG 30/2003

W3 PIPE SIZING – PRESSURE DROP ACROSS FITTINGS

Step 4. The equivalent length of pipework can now be added to the actual pipework in the system, thus enabling pipework and fittings to be considered as a single entity.

Alternatively, the actual pressure loss through the elbow can be found multiplying the pipe pressure drop per metre run (349·33 Pa/m) by the equivalent length of the fitting (0·88m), for example:

0·88 m x 349·33 Pa/m = 307·4 Pa,
which is the direct pressure loss through the elbow.

References

CIBSE Guide B1, *Heating*, Section 5.1.3, and appendix A1.3, 2002, ISBN 19032 8720 0
CIBSE Guide C, *Reference Data*, Section 4, 2001, ISBN 7506 5360 4
BSRIA, *Rules of Thumb*, TN 15/2001, BSRIA 2001, ISBN 086022 587 9
Lawrence Race G, *Design Checks for HVAC – A Quality Control Framework for Building Services Engineers* – sheets 26 and 44, AG 1/2002, BSRIA 2002, ISBN 0 86022 589 5

See also:

Sheet W1 Pipe sizing – General
Sheet W2 Pipe sizing – Straight lengths
Sheet W4 System resistance for pipework – Index run

DESIGN WATCHPOINTS

1. A common mistake is to apply the ζ for a tee piece to the wrong part of the branch. The values of ζ in *CIBSE Guide C* should be used with the l_e and Pa/m of the combined flow.

W4 SYSTEM RESISTANCE FOR PIPEWORK – INDEX RUN

Overview

The index run within a system is the circuit that has the highest resistance to the flow of water and supplies the index heat emitter. This is the worst case possible when considering pressure losses within a system. It is usually, but not always, the longest circuit in the system. Sometimes a shorter run with a greater number of fitting or items of equipment can be the index run.

The index pd (pressure drop) is required in order to successfully size the pump for the system. If the pump can work to the pressure demands of the index run then all other circuits will work.

To identify the index run, the pressure drop for several circuits may need to be found. The pressure drop across each length of pipe, fitting and terminal within these circuits will need to be calculated to determine the total pressure drop for each circuit. The one with the largest pressure drop will be the index.

➤ **Design tip:** Balancing a system is necessary to achieve the correct pressure losses and flow rates through the different components of a system. If the layout of the system is symmetrical, then the amount of commissioning required to balance the system is reduced. This is true for both water and air systems.

Design information required

See also sheet W1 Pipe sizing – general.

Number of circuits

Each circuit within a multi-circuit system needs to be clearly identified.

Pipe sizing details

All pipework and fittings should have been sized with Pa/m run, l_e (equivalent length) and ζ values available. Data is available from tables such as those found in section 4 of *CIBSE Guide C*.

➤ **Design tip:** Often the longest circuit is the index run but there is always the possibility of a shorter circuit with many fittings being the index run.

Calculation procedure

Step 1. Identify each section and where it begins and ends. For example, section 1 starts at the combined flow side of the tee fitting in the return, goes through the boiler and ends at the combined flow side of the tee fitting in the flow. Assign a reference to each section. Identify each fitting within each section and determine the design details: pressure drop (Pa/m), equivalent length (l_e) and (ζ).

Step 2. Identify each circuit by the sections it consists of, for example: circuit A = 1,2,3, circuit B = 2,3,4 and so on.

Step 3. Calculate all direct pressure losses across fittings and pipe work in each section

For fittings l_e x ζ x Pa/m = direct pressure drop (using l_e and Pa/m of the combined flow)

For straight pipe work use Δp_l x length.

Step 4. Add up the total direct pressure losses from each section within a circuit to give a circuit pressure drop.

Step 5. Identify the index run by examining each circuit pressure drop to identify the highest pressure drop.

Example

Identify the index run and calculate the index run pressure drop for the following two-pipe system serving two panel radiators, each rated at 4·15 kW.

Design data
Heat Emitters

For two heat emitters at 4·15 kW each, a 6% emission loss from pipework has been added when calculating the mass flow rate.

Assume a Δt of 10K across the system.

$$Cp = 4\cdot2 kJ/kgK$$
$$Q = (2\times4\cdot15)\times1\cdot06 = 8\cdot8 kw$$

From:
$$Q = \dot{m}cp\Delta t$$
$$\dot{m} = \frac{8\cdot8}{4\cdot2\times10} = 0\cdot21 kg/s$$

➤ **Design tip:** Where a required value does not appear exactly in the tables but occurs numerically between two values that are available, the corresponding information needed has been interpolated proportionally from the data at hand.

From table 4.11, a 20 mm diameter pipe at 0·2 kg/s gives a Δp_l of 200 Pa, at 0·211 kg/s gives a Δp_l of 220 Pa, therefore at 0·21 kg/s a Δp_l of 218·18 Pa is calculated.

This may also occur when calculating, values of ζ for reductions and enlargement fittings.

Step 1. Identify the different sections and their design details.

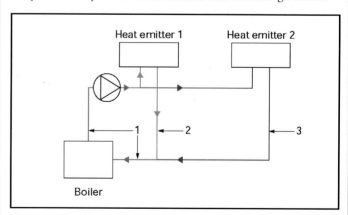

Section 1: Green
Section 2: Red
Section 3: Blue

Section details
Section 1

Straight Pipe work: length 25 m, m= 0·21 kg/s, diameter = 20 mm, l_e= 0·8, pressure drop = 218·18 Pa/m run.

Elbow: Smooth radiused inner diameter: 20 mm, ζ value: 0·75 (Table 4.48 *CIBSE Guide A*.)

Boiler: Sectional boiler ζ value: 1·5.

W4 SYSTEM RESISTANCE FOR PIPEWORK – INDEX RUN

Section 2
Straight pipe work: length 8 m, m = 0·105 kg/s, diameter = 15 mm, l_e = 0·5, pressure drop: 260 Pa/m run.
Radiator: panel radiator ζ value: 2·5.
Diverging fitting with reduction (flow and branch): ζ value = 1·64.
Converging fitting with enlargement (return and branch): ζ value 1·125, l_e of combined flow: 0·8.
Pressure drop of combined flow: 218·18 Pa/m run (both for use with the calculations for the fittings).

Section 3
Straight pipework: length 13 m, m = 0·105 kg/s, diameter = 15 mm, l_e = 0·5, pressure drop = 260 Pa/m run.
Elbow (two off): Smooth radiused inner diameter 15mm, ζ value = 0·93
Radiator: panel radiator ζ value = 2·5.
Diverging fitting with reduction (flow and straight): ζ value = 0·55,
Converging fitting with enlargement (return and straight): ζ value = 0·75,
l_e of combined flow = 0·8
Pressure drop of combined flow = 218·18 Pa/m run

Values can be found from table 4.11 of the *CIBSE Guide A* for pipe sizes and l_e, and table 4.47 and 4.48 for fittings ζ values. Values of ζ for radiators and boilers are found in table 9.1 of *Heating & Air Conditioning of Buildings* Faber & Kell, Eighth Edition. (See Design Watchpoint 1.)

Step 2. Now identify the circuits in the system;
Circuit A consists of section 1 and 2,
Circuit B consists of section 1 and 3.

Step 3. Calculate the pressure loss across each fitting and the fixture for each section. (See Design Watchpoint 2.)

There are two branches in this example, for both of the combined flow forms part of section 1; therefore as the ΔP/m to be used is that of the combined flow, the value for this example is 218·18 Pa/m.

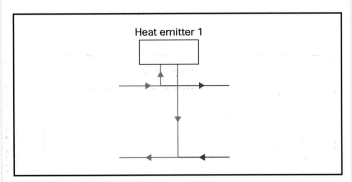

Section 1: Green
Section 2: Red
Section 3: Blue

Pressure loss for each section
Section 1
Straight pipe: 25 m x 218·18 Pa/m = 5454·5 Pa
Elbow: 0·8(l_e) x 0·75(ζ) x 218·18 Pa/m = 130·9 Pa
Boiler: 0·8(l_e) x 1·5(ζ) x 218·18 Pa/m = 261·81Pa
Total = 5847·21Pa

Section 2
Straight pipe: 8 m x 260 Pa/m = 2080 Pa
Radiator: 0·5(l_e) x 2·5(ζ) x 260 Pa/m = 325 Pa
Diverging fitting: 0·8(l_e) x 1·64(ζ) x 218·18 Pa/m = 286·25Pa
Converging fitting: 0·8(l_e) x 1·125(ζ) x 18·18 Pa/m = 196·36 Pa
Total = 2887·61Pa

Section 3
Straight pipe: 13 m x 260 Pa/m = 3380 Pa
Elbow (2 off): 0·5(l_e) x 0·93(ζ) x 260 Pa/m = 120·9 Pa
2 x 120·9 = 241·8 Pa
Radiator: 0·5(l_e) x 2·5(ζ) x 260 Pa/m = 325 Pa
Diverging fitting: 0·8(l_e) x 0·55(ζ) x 218·18 Pa/m = 95·99 Pa
Converging fitting: 0·8(l_e) x 0·75(ζ) x 218·18 Pa/m = 130·9 Pa
Total = 4173·69 Pa

Step 4. Add up total section losses for each circuit.
Circuit A Total pressure loss = 5847·21Pa + 2887·61Pa
= 8734·82 Pa, (8·73 kPa)
Circuit B Total pressure loss = 5847·21Pa + 4173·69Pa
= 10 020·9Pa, (10·02kPa)

Step 5. The index circuit in this example is Circuit B.

➢ **Design tip:** Often, as in this case, the index circuit is obvious by inspection. But, if in doubt, check all circuits. Otherwise there is a risk of undersizing the pump and poor system performance.

References
CIBSE Guide A, *Environmental Design,* 1999, ISBN 0 900 953 969
CIBSE Guide B1, *Heating,* Section 5.1.3, and appendix A1.3, 2002, ISBN 19032 8720 0
CIBSE Guide C, *Reference Data,* Section 4, 2001, ISBN 7506 5360 4
BSRIA, *Rules of Thumb,* TN 15/2001, BSRIA 2001, ISBN 086022 587 9
Lawrence Race G, *Design Checks for HVAC – A Quality Control Framework for Building Services Engineers* – sheets 26 and 44, AG 1/2002, BSRIA 2002, ISBN 0 86022 589 5
Heating & Air Conditioning of Buildings, Eighth Edition, Faber & Kell. ISBN 075 064 642 X

See also:
See Sheet W1 Pipe sizing – General
Sheet W2 Pipe sizing – Straight lengths
Sheet W3 Pipe sizing – Pressure drop across fittings
Sheet W5 Pump sizing.

DESIGN WATCHPOINTS

1. This example has the same heat emitters in both circuits. This may not always be the case.
2. When calculating the pressure loss through a fitting such as the branch fittings in this example, the ΔP/m of the combined flow is used.

W5 PUMP SIZING

Overview

Pumps are required to transport the required fluid at a given mass flow rate around a system against the resistance to flow.

Centrifugal pumps are normally used for most building services applications. There are other types of pumps, such as positive displacement pumps, that are normally used in applications where high viscosity fluid is the system medium, such as heavy fuel oil. The two main designs of pumps that are used in building services are the in-line pump and the end-suction pump.

The basic information required to size a pump is the total mass flow rate required for the system and the total pressure drop (the index pressure drop).

Once these details have been confirmed, the next step is to determine what configuration of pumps are to be used (such as single, series or parallel), and then to compare the pump performance curve or characteristic to the system performance curve or characteristic. These issues are explained below and can be determined graphically or by calculation.

Pump laws

Various pump laws show the relationships between pressure, flow rate, efficiency and power. These can be used to calculate each factor:

$$Q \propto N$$
$$P \propto N^2$$
$$W \propto N^3$$
$$P \propto \rho$$
$$W \propto \rho$$
$$Q \propto D^3$$
$$P \propto D^2$$
$$W \propto D^5$$

Where:
 Q = volume flow rate
 N = speed
 P = pressure developed
 W = power
 D = diameter of the impeller
 ρ = density.

The fundamental fluid flow laws can be found in various sources ranging from guides such as *CIBSE Guide B2,* section 5.11, to text books such as *Woods Practical Guide to Fan Engineering.*

➤ **Design tip:** When using the pump laws only change one variable at a time. The value of the factors used will be individual to the pump, and the effect of changing one variable can be found by using the pump laws. If more that one factor is changed at any one time you may effectively be creating a different pump.

System characteristics

The system performance can be expressed in the form of the equation $\Delta P = RQ^2$ for turbulent flow. The constant R is required as the equation is derived from $P \propto Q^2$. Most building services systems will use the turbulent flow equation.

Graph 1 shows the system characteristic on a pressure and volume flow rate graph.

Graph 1

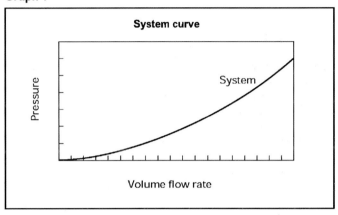

Any system will have a resistance to flow due to the fittings, components, (such as heat exchangers) and the materials used. The flow of fluid through a system will vary according to the pressure developed by the pump.

Pump characteristics

Changes can be made easily to the points of operation by changing the speed of the pump. In more extreme cases either the pump impeller or the entire pump can be changed.

The pump characteristic curve shown below is also on a graph with pressure and volume flow rate axis. In the following examples where pumps are compared to one another, it is assumed that all pumps are individually identical in duty.

A pump curve for a single pump is shown in Graph 2:

Graph 2

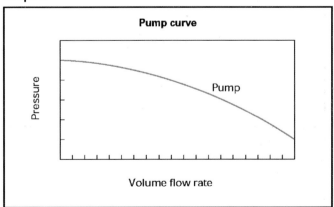

W5 PUMP SIZING

When a system performance curve and pump performance are plotted on the same graph, the intersection is the operating point for that particular pump and system combination (see Graph 3). This is the point where the operating pressure and flow rate are the same for the system and pump performance curves. This is not necessarily the desired operating point.

Graph 3

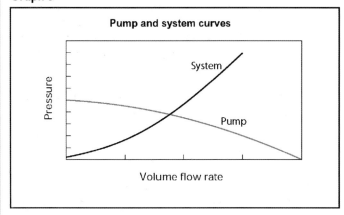

Pump and system curves

Dual pumps may sometimes be used for various reasons, such as for extra flow or to handle a high system resistance. It may be that the decision to install dual pumps for additional power instead of a single larger pump has been made due to economic costs.

Dual series pumps
When comparing the pump characteristics of a single pump and dual pumps in series (all identical), the pressure is doubled for a given volume flow rate. The combined pumps give a new curve.

Graph 4

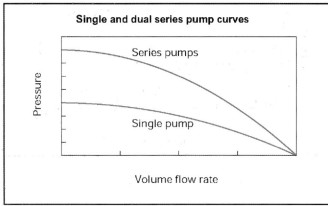

Single and dual series pump curves

When the system curve is also plotted on the same graph the new operating point can be determined and compared with that of a single pump (see Graph 5).

Graph 5

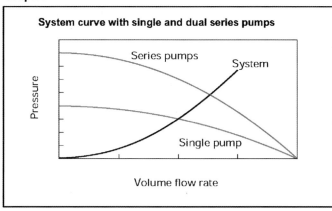

System curve with single and dual series pumps

Dual parallel pumps
The same applies with parallel pumps where the volume is doubled for a given pressure.

Graph 6

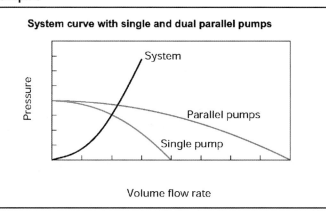

System curve with single and dual parallel pumps

Design Information Required
Details of pipework system layout
Including lengths and fittings, materials and insulation details.

Details of possible locations
Such as plant room location and layout, space available for installation of pumps and drives, permissible weights.

Criticality of system served

Electrical supply
One or three phase.

Pump type
Centrifugal (end-suction, in line, immersed rotor), displacement (helical or rotary).

Drive type
Belt or direct.

Noise criteria

W5 PUMP SIZING

Key design inputs
- Details of fluid, for example water, glycol solution or oil.
- Design flow and return temperatures (^{0}C)
- System mass flow rates (kg/s)
- System pressure drops (Pa)
- Ambient conditions including the surrounding air temperature (^{0}C)

Design outputs
- Schematic of pump layout installation, mounting and pipework connections
- Schedule of pump types, flow rates, pressure and efficiencies including motor requirements, drive type and adjustment, speed control and stand by provision
- Media details, such as water/refrigerant, and temperature.
- A schedule of electricity supply requirements

Calculation procedure
Step 1. Calculate the index run pressure drop and total system mass flow rate.

Step 2. Convert mass flow rate to volume flow rate in l/s.

Step 3. Determine system equations constant R. This can be done by substituting the required ΔP and Q into the equation $\Delta P = RQ^2$ and then solving for R.

Step 4. Select a pump that will operate within the required parameters and plot the system and pump characteristics on the same graph.

Step 5. Determine the operating point. Identify operating pressure and flow rate.

Step 6. Calculate pump speed to achieve required values or select another pump.

➢ **Design tip:** With belt-driven pumps it is easy to vary the speed by changing the pulleys. If the pump is inverter - driven this can be done automatically.

➢ **Design tip:** If you use an additional margin with the required pressure drop to allow for differences between design pipe work layout and physical installations on site, do so carefully, as over - sizing a pump will only result in excess energy usage.

Example
A system has a volume flow rate requirement of 1 l/s with an index run ΔP of 30 kPa. Find an appropriate pump.

Step 1. and 2. Pressure drop and volume flow rate are available in the units required.

Step 3. The constant R in the system characteristic curve equation can be calculated as shown below:

$\Delta P = RQ^2$
Index run pd = 30 kPa
Volume flow rate = 1 l/s
$30 = R \times 1^2$
ie $R = \dfrac{30}{1} = 30$
$\Delta P = 30Q^2$

Step 4. A pump needs to be selected that will work within the parameters of pressure and volume flow rate already stated. Selection will also depend on the type of system and design features of the pump. (See Design Watchpoint 1.)

Once a pump has been selected that can work in the range required, the pump and system curve should be plotted on a single graph. Some manufacturers will provide a range of pump curves on a graph with efficiency and power curves underneath. If this is the case then the system curve can be drawn directly onto the graph and the operating points identified quickly. For this example it is assumed that the pump data is given in table form.

A manufacturer's catalogue gives the following information for a centrifugal pump operating at 12 rev/s:

P pressure (kPa)
Q volume Flow Rate (l/s)

P	49·38	47·5	44·38	40	34·38	27·5	19·38
Q	0·25	0·5	0·75	1	1·25	1·5	1·75

This particular pump has the following equation:

$\Delta P = 50 - 10Q^2$

With the system equation the two can be solved simultaneously, or the pressure against volume flow rate for both equations can be plotted to find the intersection point.

Pump and system curves
Graph 7

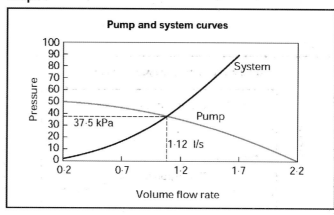

Step 5. The operating point occurs when the two curves intersect, 1·12 l/s at 37·5 kPa

Step 6. As 1·12 l/s is too high, the pump will need to be slowed down in order to achieve the required flow rate. Alternatively, a different pump may give a closer value. This is worth considering when comparing the efficiency of different pumps at different speeds and pressures.

W5 PUMP SIZING

By using the pump law $Q \propto N$:

$$\frac{Q_{des}}{Q} = \frac{N_{des}}{N}$$

Where:

Q_{des} = desired volume flow rate

N_{des} = desired pump rotational speed

The required speed can be determined that is needed to provide 1·0 l/s.

Therefore:

$$N_{des} = \frac{1 \cdot 0}{1 \cdot 12} \times 12 = 10 \cdot 7 \text{ rev/s}$$

This can also be achieved by using the pump law $P \propto N^2$, for example:

$$\frac{P_{des}}{P} = \frac{N_{des}^2}{N^2}$$

Therefore:

$$N_{des}^2 = \frac{30}{37 \cdot 5} \times 12^2 = 115 \cdot 2$$

$$N_{des} = \sqrt{115 \cdot 2} = 10 \cdot 7 \text{ rev/s}$$

➢ **Design tip:** A functioning pump will have operating losses such belt or drive losses. The pump and system performance curves do not take this into account.

➢ **Design tip**: The use of inverters to control the speed of the pump is the most efficient method of controlling and restricting the flow. The cost and maintenance requirements of the inverter need to be considered. An alternate method is to adjust a globe valve on the pump discharge side to achieve the required flow. However the latter method is wasteful of energy and only works if all other parameters remain constant.

Net Positive Suction Head (NPSH)

(See Design Watchpoint 2.) The term head is often used to mean pressure developed by a pump or column of liquid. Centrifugal pumps are not able to develop suction pressure unless filled with fluid first (primed). Care is needed to ensure that at the suction of a pump, the absolute pressure of the fluid exceeds the vapour pressure of the fluid. This is particularly important when working with hot fluids.

If a pump is drawing water from some point below the centre line of the impellor, the vertical height through which that water is lifted must not be sufficient to cause cavitation.

Cavitation is where small pockets (bubbles) of vapour of the fluid are created due to incorrect pressures. As the bubbles move through the pump, they change in pressure causing them to collapse. This creates noise and can cause damage to the pump in the suction line or to the impellor surface.

Net positive suction head is defined in *BS 5316 Part 1* as the total inlet head, plus the head corresponding to the atmospheric pressure, minus the head corresponding to the vapour pressure. The total inlet head is the sum of static, positive and velocity heads at the inlet section of the pump.

References

BSI, *BS 5316 Part 1, Acceptable tests for Centrifugal, Mixed Flow and Axial Pumps; Class C Tests,* 1976

Parsloe C J, *Variable speed pumping in heating and cooling circuits,* AG 14/99, BSRIA 1999, ISBN 086022533X

Lawrence Race G, *Design Checks for HVAC – A Quality Control Framework for Building Services Engineers* – sheet 47, AG 1/2002, BSRIA 2002, ISBN 0 86022 589 5

See also:

Sheet W1 Pipe sizing – General

Sheet W2 Pipe sizing – Straight lengths

CIBSE Guide B1, *Heating*, Section 5.1.4, 2002, ISBN 1 903 487 200

CIBSE Guide B2, *Ventilation and Air Conditioning*, Section 5.11, 2001, ISBN 1 903287 16 2

CIBSE Guide C, *Reference Data,* Section 4, 2001, ISBN 7506 5360 4

DESIGN WATCHPOINTS

1. When selecting a pump check the point of operation. If the pump selected is operating on a flat part of the curve, controlling volume flow rate can be difficult as the pressure is fairly constant for a changing volume flow rate.
2. Net positive suction head (NPSH), can be a complex area. If errors are made there can be potential system problems. It is only briefly discussed here as it is advised that a junior engineer should consult a senior engineer.

W6 WATER SYSTEM PRESSURISATION

Overview

The density of a fluid changes significantly with temperature leading to a change in fluid volume. For example water entering a heating system at 4°C will expand by 2·9% in volume if heated up to 80°C, and by 5% if heated up to 110°C (as in medium pressure hot water systems). Hence a 1000 litre system will expand to 1050 litres if heated from 4°C to 110°C. If this is not catered for, the fluid volume expansion could create an excessive rise in system pressure and cause serious safety or operational problems.

Most HVAC wet systems do not operate at a constant temperature, but will cycle in temperature during operation or when starting up. Although the mass will remain constant the fluid volume will expand and contract. The amount of expansion will depend on the type of system, heating or cooling, and the operating temperatures. (See Design Watchpoint 1.)

Allowance must be made within the system for these variations. This is normally done by installing an expansion vessel in sealed (closed) systems or a feed and expansion tank in a vented (open) system such as domestic hot water systems. (See Design Watchpoint 2.)

Design information required

System type and fluid type and temperature
Designers should state the conditions of hot water, chilled water and the exact composition of any water and glycol mixture to determine the density and expansion characteristics of the fluid.

Initial pressure (kPa or bars)
This consists of the system static pressure (the height of the system circuit above the plant) together with a reasonable safety pressure margin. (The values for pressure margins for water systems are given in table 1)

Expansion factor
This can be calculated using information on density (such as $V = m/\rho$). Figures for the expansion of water are given in table 1 according to temperature.

Total system volume (litres)
This can be determined from pipe work and the plant associated with the system.

Maximum allowable system pressure (kPa or bars)
This should be carried out as a safety cross-check.

Key design inputs
- Total system volume (litres)
- System static pressure (kPa or bars)
- System flow and return temperatures (°C)
- Maximum allowable system pressure (kPa or bars)

Design outputs
- Vessel parameters allowing selection from manufacturer's data
- The safety-valve pressure-setting for the system

Calculation procedure

➢ **Design tip:** Ensure that you work in consistent units of pressure throughout, such as all kPa or all bar. One bar is 100 kPa.

Step 1. Calculate initial pressure as follows:
Initial pressure equals static pressure plus the pressure margin (from table 1 below).

Step 2. Calculate expansion volume:
Expansion volume equals the expansion factor (table 1 below) times the total system volume.

Step 3. Select a vessel to accept the expansion volume with at least a 10% margin. The maximum vessel working pressure is 6 bar (see: *BS4814: 1990 Sealed heating systems*).

➢ **Design tip:** Selecting a larger volume vessel can reduce the final system pressure.

Step 4. Calculate the acceptance factor:

$$\text{Acceptance factor} = \frac{\text{Expansion volume}}{\text{Total vessel volume}}$$

Step 5. Calculate the final pressure:

$$\frac{\text{Initial pressure} + \text{acceptance factor}}{1 \cdot 0 - \text{acceptance factor}}$$

Step 6. Determine the required safety valve pressure setting for the system.

➢ **Design tip**: The system safety-valve setting should be no less than 0·7 bar above the final calculated pressure. This allows at least a 0·35 bar differential above the high-pressure alarm.

Table 1: Expansion factors for water.

Maximum temperature °C	Pressure margin bar	Expansion factor water
20	0· 5	0· 002
30	0· 5	0· 005
40	0· 5	0· 008
50	0· 5	0· 012
60	0· 5	0· 017
70	0· 5	0· 023
80	0· 5	0· 03

Example
Determine the expansion volume for the following heating system and select an appropriate expansion vessel and the final pressure.

Design data
Total system volume 4500 litres
Static pressure (15 m) 1·5 bar
System flow and return temperatures 82/71°C
Max allowable system pressure 4·0 bar

© BSRIA BG 30/2003

W6 WATER SYSTEM PRESSURISATION

Vessel Selection

Step 1.
Pressure margin = 0·5 bar from table 1,
Initial pressure = 1·5 + 0·5 = 2 bar

Step 2.
Expansion factor = 0·03 from table 1,
Expansion volume = 0·03 x 4500 = 135 litres

Step 3.
Select vessel to accept 135 litres expansion volume with at least 10% margin.

Such as at least 135 + 13·5 = 148·5 litres

A vessel with 500 litres volume has been selected from manufacturer's data.

Step 4.
Acceptance factor =

$$\frac{135}{500} = 0·27$$

Step 5. Calculate final pressure =

$$\frac{\text{Initial pressure} + \text{acceptance factor}}{1·0 - \text{acceptance factor}}$$

$$= \frac{2·0 + 0·27}{1·0 - 0·27} = 3·109 \text{ bar}$$

Step 6. Safety valve setting:
The system safety valve set pressure should be no less than 0·7 bar above the calculated final pressure.

Therefore the system safety valve should be set at a minimum of 3·109 + 0·7 = 3·809 bar

References

CIBSE Guide B1, *Heating*, Section 4.3.9 and appendix A1.1, 2001, ISBN 1 903 487 200
CIBSE Guide C, *Reference Data*, 2001, ISBN 7506 5360 4
BSRIA, *Rules of Thumb*, TN 15/2001, BSRIA 2001, ISBN 086022 587 9
Lawrence Race G, *Design Checks for HVAC – A Quality Control Framework for Building Services Engineers* – sheets 26 and 44, AG 1/2002, BSRIA 2002, ISBN 0 86022 589 5
BSI, BS 4814: 1990, *Sealed heating systems*, BSI 1990, ISBN 0580 176908
BSI, BS 5449: 1990, *Specification for forced circulation hot water central heating systems*, BSI 1990, ISBN 0580172937
BSI, BS 7074: 1989, *Application, selection and installation of expansion vessels and ancillary equipment for sealed water systems* Parts 1, 2 and 3, BSI 1989, ISBN 0580171450, ISBN 0580171469, ISBN 0580171477

See also:
Sheet W2 Pipe sizing – Straight lengths
Sheet W3 Pipe sizing – Pressure drop across fittings
Sheet W4 System resistance for pipework – Index run

DESIGN WATCHPOINTS

1. Note that even chilled water systems need to allow for expansion, as the water in the system may be starting at an ambient temperature of 20°C or higher if idle for long periods in summer.
2. Sealed fluid systems must include appropriate safety features such as safety valves and high pressure alarms.

The following section contains nine building services engineering topic areas related to the design of air flow distribution systems.

The following two pages contain flow charts of the relevant design and calculation processes. The first flow chart shows the nine topics within this section.

The second flow chart provides an overview of the process, showing some of the many related topics that need to be considered in the design of air flow distribution systems. The boxes highlighted in blue show an area that is fully or partially covered within one of the nine topic areas in this section, or in the rest of the guidance, along with the appropriate reference numbers.

© BSRIA BG 30/2003

FLOW CHART I – TOPICS WITHIN THIS SECTION

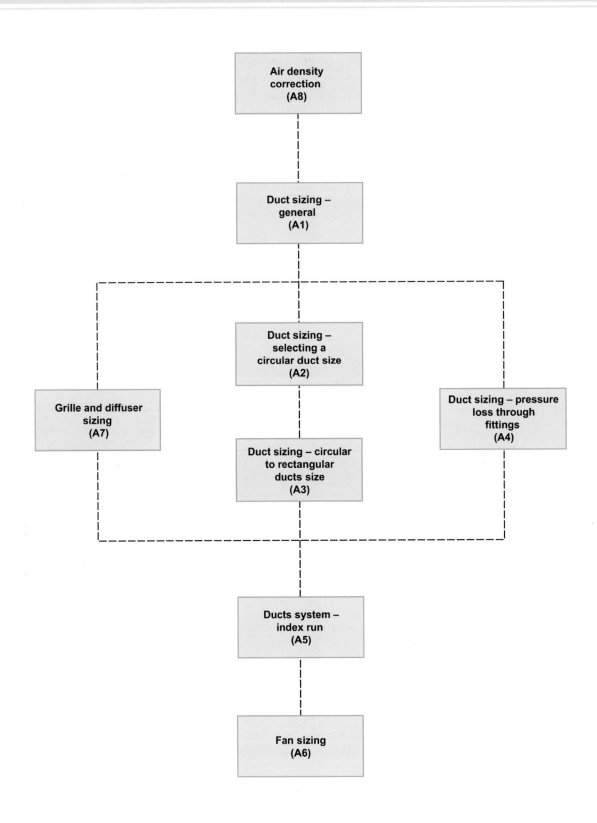

© BSRIA BG 30/2003

FLOW CHART 2 – OVERVIEW OF SYSTEM DESIGN PROCESS

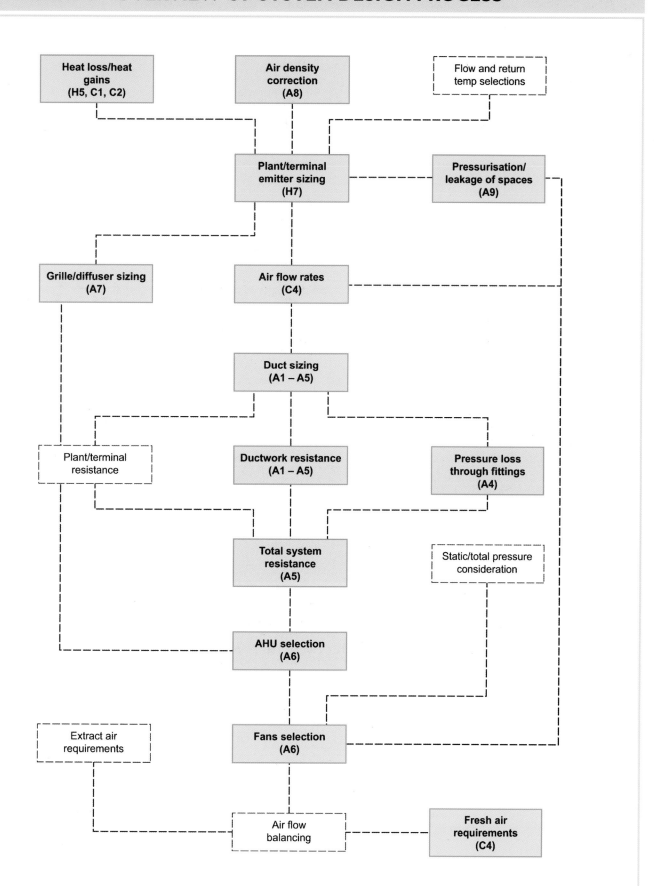

This chart shows the design areas relevant to this design process. Where design areas are wholly or partially discussed in this document the relevant sheet references are given in brackets

© BSRIA BG 30/2003

A1   DUCT SIZING – GENERAL

Overview

Duct sizing is used to determine the correct duct sizes to deliver the air volume required for ventilation, heating and cooling, or to remove contaminants. Air is a fluid and therefore the fundamental principles of fluid flow apply (the same D'Arcy fluid flow equation as given for pipes on sheet W1).

The equation (known as the D'Arcy Equation) above is written as:

$$\Delta P = \frac{\lambda L}{d} \times \frac{1}{2}\rho v^2$$

Where:
- ΔP = pressure loss (Pa)
- ρ = density of the fluid (kg/m^3)
- λ = friction factor
- l = length of duct (m)
- v = mean velocity of water flow (m/s)
- d = internal duct diameter (m).

There may be several duct size options that are initially acceptable but the final choice of duct size will depend on the cost of materials and installation, the space available and the energy costs of moving the air.

Duct sizing can be carried out either manually or using a spreadsheet or computer sizing package. However, in all cases, correct input data must be used and the output cross-checked.

There are several methods available for sizing a ductwork system. These are the constant pressure-drop method (also known as constant pressure gradient), the constant velocity method, static regain (*CIBSE B3* Ductwork Section 4.3) and the T-method (see *1997 ASHRAE Fundamentals Handbook* (SI), Chapter 32 Duct Design, page 32.21).

The constant pressure drop method is the one most widely used for normal air conditioning applications.

The constant velocity method is used in applications such as exhaust ventilation where a minimum velocity for carrying dust is important, or in applications where noise pollution is unacceptable and the duct velocities need to be limited. Where these conditions apply it is normally used either for sections of a duct system, or a whole duct system if it has a simple layout.

Static regain is normally used with a computer package for high velocity systems where the duct velocity pressure is adequate to give static-pressure regain at the end of the run without creating excessively low duct velocities. Normally this method is used for the main duct in the system, while the branches off the main duct are sized using the constant pressure-drop method.

Design information required
Client requirements

It may be obvious that the design of the system should meet the requirements of the client but these details will determine many choices made in the design process. It is important to agree with the client on requirements and main priorities.

Required supply air condition
This will enable the relevant air properties such as density to be determined.

Type of system supplied
This will determine what is acceptable in terms of flow temperatures, pressure drops and, noise level.

Ambient conditions
These are the conditions through which the ductwork system will run. This will affect heat losses and gains to the ductwork system.

Duct material
Ducts can be made from galvanised steel, aluminium, plaster or plastic. This determines duct roughness and hence the flow characteristics and duct pressure losses.

➢ **Design tip:** Galvanised steel ductwork is the most common material used, hence the duct-sizing chart figure 4.2 in *CIBSE Guide C* is for galvanised steel. For other types of materials used such as plastered ducts and aluminium ducts a correction factor from tables 4.37 – to 4.39 will need to be applied to the pressure drop.

Duct insulation
Designers should determine whether ducts are to be insulated and, if so, the details of the insulation. Although the temperature differentials are not normally as great as can occur with water flow systems, there may be occasions when losses and gains to and from the ductwork system will need to be considered.

Duct system layout
Determine the distribution space available both horizontally and vertically, the duct lengths, and the number and type of fittings.

Key design inputs
- Design volume flow rates in m^3/s
- Limiting duct pressure loss in Pa/m
- Limiting flow velocity in m/s

Design outputs
- A schematic of ductwork layout and associated plant showing required volume flow rates
- A schedule of duct sizes and lengths, and fittings

Design approach
1. The design process should minimise breakout noise, installation and operating costs.

➢ **Design tip:** With noise, the design criteria may include a maximum noise rating permissible by the building services installation. Acceptable noise ratings for different environments are available in *CIBSE Guide A* 1999, Section 1, table 1.1 and 1.17.

➢ **Design tip:** When designing a system it can be easy to overlook the installation costs incurred by choice of equipment and materials, or by limiting factors such as restrictions within a building's layout.

A1 DUCT SIZING – GENERAL

2. Ductwork layouts should be as short as possible; minimise tight bends and ensure the system is as self-balancing as possible.

3. High pressure drops will result in smaller duct sizes but fan running costs will be higher.

4. Low pressure drops result in lower fan costs but duct sizes will be larger.

5. When designing a duct system, the designer should use the duct type and material appropriate for the project and application. The basic shapes of ductwork available are rectangular, flat oval and circular.

> **Design tip:** There are standard sizes for the different shapes of ductwork available. Rectangular ductwork can also be made to the dimensions required, but the economic implications for the project should be checked.

6. Contoured flexible ducting, although convenient and easy to use, does have a considerably higher $\Delta P/l$ compared to fixed rectangular ducts. Fittings such as reducers and enlargements are costly, particularly when both dimensions are being changed in the same fitting. When using these types of fittings only one dimension should be reduced or enlarged at each fitting, for example fitting with height reduction and constant width.

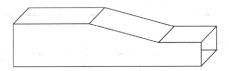

Whichever method of sizing is used, it is important to check the $\Delta P/l$ at each section and the velocity for the required volume flow rate and the chosen duct size. This is particularly important when adjusting a duct size for economic reasons or for imposed limitations such as lack of space.

7. While flow in ductwork is normally turbulent, the design should minimise the occurrence of excessively turbulent flow as this increases the pressure drop and wastes energy in higher fan running costs. Excessive turbulence can be caused by obstructions to flow, such as sharp changes in direction and rough surfaces. Excessive turbulence will increase the maximum required velocity.

> **Design tip:** Avoid sudden changes in air flow direction, duct size or shape, such as abrupt enlargements.

> **Design tip:** Circular ductwork provides a lower pressure drop (ΔP) per unit length than an equivalent rectangular duct. This is because the circular duct provides less opportunity for the airflow within it to be excessively turbulent (in other words no corners or rough edges), so therefore most of the airflow is laminar.

If rectangular ductwork is used then the amount of excessively turbulent flow can be kept to a minimum by choosing a duct that is as near to a circle as possible in other words square, or at least with dimension ratios as close to 1:1 as possible.

Aspect ratios

When using rectangular duct it is important to try and keep the aspect ratio at 1:1, or if not, as close as possible to 1:1. As the aspect ratio increases, the frictional resistance increases and therefore the pressure loss increases. This is because the wetted perimeter of a piece of ductwork with an aspect ratio of 4:1 is larger than the wetted perimeter of a piece of ductwork with an aspect ratio of 1:1 with the same cross-sectional area. The smallest wetted perimeter for the same cross sectional area would be achieved by using a circular duct.

Given a cross sectional area of 0.5 m^2, the following dimensions would be required as follows:

A circular duct
$$Area = \pi r^2$$
$$Perimeter = 2\pi r$$
$$0.5 = \pi r^2$$
$$0.5 \div \pi = r^2$$
$$r = \sqrt{(0.5 \div \pi)}$$
$$r = 0.398m$$

therefore the wetted perimeter of the duct is
$$P = 2\pi 0.398$$
$$P = 2.50m$$

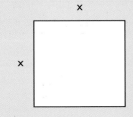

A rectangular duct with an aspect ratio of 1:1
$$Area = x^2$$
$$Perimeter = 4x$$
$$0.5 = x^2$$
$$x = \sqrt{0.5}$$
$$x = 0.707m$$

therefore the wetted perimeter of the duct is
$$P = 4 \times 0.707$$
$$P = 2.82m$$

A rectangular duct with an aspect ratio of 4:1
$$Area = 4x^2$$
$$Perimeter = 10x$$
$$0.5 = 4x^2$$
$$x = \sqrt{(0.5 \div 4)}$$
$$x = 0.353m$$

therefore the wetted perimeter of the duct is
$$P = 10 \times 0.353$$
$$P = 3.53m$$

A1   DUCT SIZING – GENERAL

Engineers are recommended to not use an aspect ratio larger than 4:1 as the frictional resistance becomes too high. The wetted perimeter increases with the aspect ratio but also with flexibility of the duct wall. This can lead to increased noise breakout and the possibility of drumming. (See Design Watchpoint 1.)

Once the initial duct design has been made the dimensions should be put onto a schematic or layout drawing of the system. The system below has had the different sections of ductwork sized according to the criteria given (see sheet A3 –Circular to rectangular duct, examples 1,2 and3). The results of the initial sizing without any correction is as shown in the layout drawing.

➤ **Design tip:** Writing the dimensions down in a cross with the volume flow rates (Q), velocities (v) and pressure drop (ΔP) helps to quickly cross check that limitations on velocities and pressure drops have not been exceeded, and helps to communicate the required design as in this example:

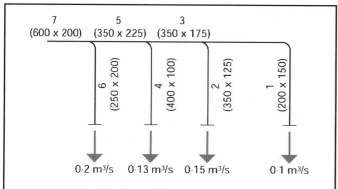

System 1 – initial dimensions

8.   If the initial sizes were actually used, the resultant duct system would look something like the diagram opposite, which is obviously unacceptable, expensive and difficult to install.

The diagram is not to scale and, of course is only in 2D, but it does give an idea of the result of using non-standard sizes and changing both dimensions of the duct at the same time when reducing (or enlarging). In practice only one side is changed at each volume flow difference and this would normally be to standard manufacturer's sizes. Of course the pressure drops through each section would need to be checked to make sure that they are within acceptable limits for the type of system.

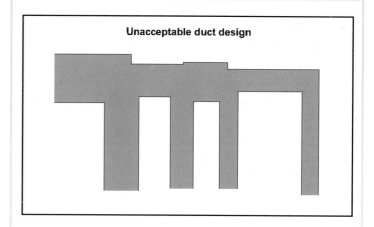

Unacceptable duct design

9.   It is at this point junior engineers should go back through the duct-sizing procedure remembering to consider dimension ratios, changing one dimension at a time for fittings and the range of standard sizes and costs of using non-standard sizes. A degree of judgement may be required from experienced engineers.

After taking into consideration ratios etc the final dimensions of system 1 are as follows:

System 1 – final dimensions

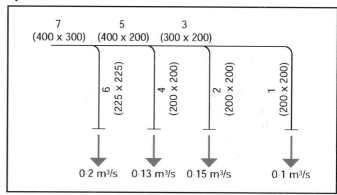

Rules of thumb – design data
Typical air velocities and pressure drops
Low velocity systems: 3-6 m/s with a maximum pressure drop of 1 Pa/m.

High velocity systems: 7·5-15 m/s with a maximum pressure drop of 8 Pa/m. (See Design Watchpoint 4.)

Table 4.35 of *CIBSE Guide C* gives typical velocities through air handling units and components.

Section 3.2 of *CIBSE Guide B3* gives velocities and noise ratings that are suitable for different applications.

In practice figure 4.2 *CIBSE Guide C* is used for duct sizing using either the constant pressure drop or the velocity method.

© BSRIA BG 30/2003

A1   DUCT SIZING – GENERAL

References

CIBSE Guide A, *Environmental* Design, 1999,
ISBN 0 900 953 969

CIBSE Guide B3, *Ductwork*, Section 3.2, Duct air velocities,
2002, ISBN 1 903287 20 0

CIBSE Guide C, *Reference Data*, Section 4, 2001,
ISBN 7506 5360 4

HVCA, *Specification for Sheet Metal Ductwork DW/144*,
Appendix A, 2000, ISBN 0903783274

HVCA, *A Practical Guide to Ductwork Leakage Testing DW/143*,
2000, ISBN 0903783304

BSRIA, *Rules of Thumb*, TN 15/2001, BSRIA 2001,
ISBN 086022 587 9

Lawrence Race G, *Design Checks for HVAC – A Quality Control
Framework for Building Services Engineers* – sheets 27 and 45,
AG 1/2002, BSRIA 2002, ISBN 0 86022 589 5

*Building Regulations Approved Document Part L2 – Conservation of
fuel and power.* Edition clause 1.67, 2002 Edition,
ISBN 0 11753 610 5

See also:

Sheet A2 Duct sizing – Selecting a circular duct size

Sheet A3 Duct sizing – Circular to rectangular ducts

Sheet A4 Duct sizing – Pressure loss through fittings

Sheet A5 Duct system – Index run

Sheet A8 Air density correction

CIBSE Guide B3, *Ductwork*, Section 2, Strategic design issues,
2002, ISBN 1 903287 20 0

DESIGN WATCHPOINTS

1. Restrictions in available space may be an obvious factor to
    consider when sizing a duct but it is worthwhile remembering to
    check this, for example, ceiling voids of fixed depth. Also
    excessively sized risers to take ductwork use potentially lettable
    floor space.

2. Air density changes with pressure and temperature (see sheet
    A8). Table 4.36 from *CIBSE Guide C* gives air densities at different
    temperatures at a constant pressure of 1·01325 bar. Equation
    4.17 from *CIBSE Guide A* can be used to adjust the density if the
    air pressure changes. The equation includes a value for density at
    any air temperature, and this can be taken from table 4.36.

3. Check that both flow velocities and pressure drops are within
    acceptable limits at each section of the duct, whether during
    initial sizing or final sizing.

4. Leakage from a duct system is undesirable. If a system leaks too
    much air the running costs of the system will increase and the
    system may not provide the required volume and quality of air.
    The *HVCA Specification for Sheet Metal Ductwork DW/144 appendix
    A: air leakage from ductwork*, contains details on acceptable limits
    of duct leakage and should be read in conjunction with *DW/143 A
    practical guide to Ductwork leakage testing.*

5. For buildings with mechanical ventilation and air conditioning,
    part of the requirements of the *Approved Document L2*, 2002
    Edition (The requirements L2 (e)), are that provisions are made
    so that no more energy needs to be used than is reasonable in
    the circumstances. This applies to a total area of 200 m^2 that is to
    be served by mechanical ventilation or air conditioning systems.
    For systems in new buildings the specific fan power should be no
    greater than 2·0 W/l/s. For refurbished buildings where an
    existing system exists that is to be substantially altered, the
    specific fan power should be no greater than 3·0 W/l/s
    (Approved Document L2, 2002 Edition clause 1.67).

A2 DUCT SIZING – SELECTING A CIRCULAR DUCT SIZE

Overview

The duct sizing given in figure 4.2 of *CIBSE Guide C* shows the flow of air at 20°C in circular galvanised steel ducts.

The chart relates the four variables needed for duct and fan sizing:
Volume flow rate (q) (m^3/s)
Velocity (v) (m/s)
Pressure drop per unit length (ΔP) (Pa/m)
Diameter (m).

In order to use the chart, two of the variables need to be known or selected and the remaining two can then be found from the chart.

A representation of figure 4.2 *Guide C* is shown below. A line representing a single value for each variable has been drawn to show the angle at which the different variables lie on the chart.

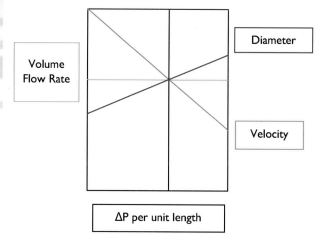

While the volume flow rate (q) is usually known from the ventilation requirements and/or heating/cooling loads, one other factor is needed. The second value is either a pre-determined pressure drop per unit length or a pre-determined velocity, (hence the constant pressure drop and velocity methods for duct sizing).

Where a length of duct has a given or found ΔP per unit length, of say, 2 Pa and the piece of duct in question has a length of 20 m, the total pressure drop across that length is obviously 40 Pa.

Key design inputs
• Volume flow rate (m^3/s)
• Pressure drop per unit length (Pa)
• Velocity (m/s)

Design output
• For each part of a ductwork system, engineers must determine the required volume flow rate, the preliminary duct size and the pressure drop per metre run and velocity for that section. (On this sheet circular duct sizing is covered; circular to rectangular duct dimensions are covered on sheet A3.)

Velocity method

Once the known volume flow rate q and a suitable value for velocity is selected, they can be drawn on the chart (shown in red). Where the two lines cross, values for pressure drop and diameter can be read off the chart.

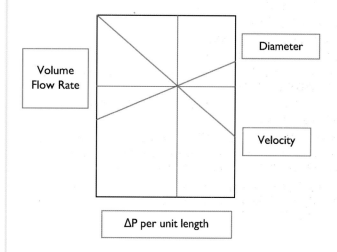

Example I
A client asks for a duct system to be sized. Part of that duct needs to be sized with the following criteria: a volume flow rate of 0·8 m^3/s and a velocity of 8 m/s. What is the corresponding diameter and pressure drop per unit length?

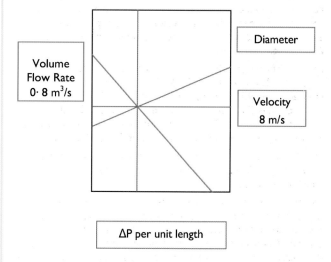

1. Using figure 4.2 *CIBSE Guide C*, draw on the lines that correspond to volume flow rate and velocity, this has been highlighted in red on diagram 3.
2. Mark on the chart where the volume flow rate and velocity intersect.
3. Read off the associated pressure drop per unit length and duct diameter. The pressure drop per unit length is 2 Pa/m, with a circular diameter of 0·36 m.

A2   DUCT SIZING – SELECTING A CIRCULAR DUCT SIZE

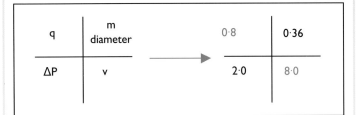

(See Design Watchpoint 1.)

Example 2

It is decided that the pressure drop is too high and therefore unacceptable. It is decided that the velocity can be reduced but must be at a minimum of 6 m/s and the volume flow rate must be maintained at 0.8 m³/s. Find the diameter and pressure drop per unit length using decreased velocity.

1. Using figure 4.2 *CIBSE Guide C*, draw on the lines that correspond to volume flow rate and velocity.
2. Mark on the chart where the volume flow rate and velocity intersect.
3. Read off the associated pressure drop per unit length and diameter.

The pressure drop per unit length is 1.05 Pa/m (slightly over 1 Pa/m), with a circular diameter of 0.42 m.

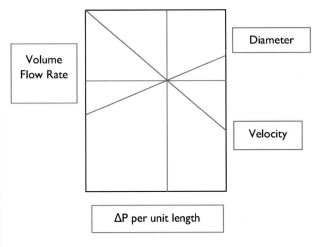

(See Design Watchpoint 2.)

Where greater accuracy is required an alternative method of sizing a duct using the velocity method is by calculation, using the equations:

$$q = A v$$

Where:
   q = volume flow rate (m³/s)
   v = velocity (m/s)
   A = Area (m²)

Where:
   $A = \pi \frac{d^2}{4}$
   D = diameter (m)

Constant pressure-drop method

Once the known volume flow rate q has been highlighted on the chart, a pressure drop value is selected and also highlighted. Where the two lines cross, values of velocity and diameter can be read off the chart.

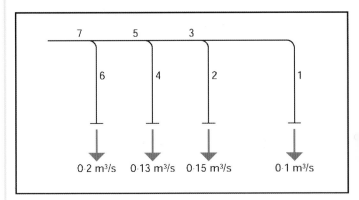

Example 3

Using the duct sizing figure 4.2 Guide C, find the circular duct sizes and corresponding velocities for each section of system 1.

System 1

Volume flow rate (q) values are known and a pressure drop of 1 Pa/m is assumed.

Volume flow rates are worked out for each section and using the *CIBSE* duct sizing chart figure 4.2 the duct diameters and velocities are determined:

Section	q m³/s	ΔP Pa/m	v m/s	Diameter mm
1	0.1	1	3.6	190
2	0.15	1	4	225
3	0.25	1	4.5	270
4	0.13	1	3.9	210
5	0.38	1	5.0	308
6	0.2	1	4.4	245
7	0.58	1	5.5	370

A2   DUCT SIZING – SELECTING A CIRCULAR DUCT SIZE

These diameters are the initial sizes found using the *CIBSE* duct sizing chart figure 4.2 with the relevant volume flow rate and maintaining a pressure drop of 1 Pa/m for each section. Many, if not all of the values for velocity and duct diameter have been interpolated by eye from the chart, therefore repeating the process may result in slightly different figures being determined.

(See Design Watchpoint 3.)

Cross-check
Velocities are within the range 3-6 m/s, which is acceptable for a low velocity system.

CIBSE Guide B3, section 4.3, Principles of design gives further details of the methods of designing a ductwork system.

References
CIBSE Guide B3, *Ductwork*, Section 4.3, Principles of design, 2002, ISBN 1 903287 20 0

CIBSE Guide C, *Reference Data,* Section 4, 2001, ISBN 7506 5360 4

BSRIA *Rules of Thumb,* TN 15/2001, BSRIA 2001, ISBN 086022 587 9

Lawrence Race G, *Design Checks for HVAC – A Quality Control Framework for Building Services Engineers* – sheets 27 and 45, AG 1/2002, BSRIA 2002, ISBN 0 86022 589 5

See also:
Sheet A1 Duct sizing – General

Sheet A3 Duct sizing – Circular to rectangular ducts

Sheet A4 Duct sizing – Pressure loss through fittings

Sheet A5 Duct system – Index run

DESIGN WATCHPOINTS

1. Beware - the duct sizing chart (figure 4.2) is logarithmic and inaccurate readings on smaller values can have a considerable impact on pressure drop; for example at duct sizes of 100-150 mm small changes can increase the pressure drop by 20-50%.

2. Don't forget that when drawing lines on charts in order to determine other values the accuracy of the lines drawn and values, read off will depend on pencil thickness and the user's accuracy.

3. Recommended sizes for ductwork can be found in *CIBSE B3 Ductwork,* Appendix A1, and standard sizes for flat oval ducts and circular ducts can be found in *HVCA Specification for Sheet Metal Ductwork DW/144.*

4. If circular ductwork is going to be used for this system, then a further review will be needed to review the practicalities of the duct sizes chosen. In other words it may be more economic from an installation viewpoint to have all branches - or at least branches 1,2 and 4 - the same size.

A3 DUCT SIZING - CIRCULAR TO RECTANGULAR DUCT

Overview

As discussed in sheet A2, using chart figure 4.2 in *CIBSE Guide C* enables the required duct diameters to be determined. However, other ductwork materials and shapes may be required for a particular application so the diameters will need to be converted to an appropriate size. For rectangular ductwork this can be done using table 4.40 from *CIBSE Guide C*, and table 4.41 allows conversion from circular to flat-oval duct.

Rectangular ducts are the most commonly used duct type for low-pressure duct systems. They are available in standard sizes but can be tailored to fit into the space available by a manufacturer to required dimensions, within reason. Joints to system components such as filters and coils are straightforward and branch connections are easily made compared to other ductwork shapes.

Circular ductwork has the lowest pressure drop per unit length. Flat-oval has a slightly higher pressure drop when compared to the equivalent rectangular duct, but the advantages of using rectangular duct often outweigh this. It may be appropriate to use a combination of duct types, such as rectangular ducting for main distribution with flexible connections to terminals or circular ducting for the main ducts with rectangular branches.

Information on standard sizes can be found in *BS EN 1506:1998 Ventilation for buildings - Sheet metal air ducts and fitting with circular cross section − Dimensions*.

Table 4.40 from *CIBSE Guide C* gives equivalent rectangular dimensions (side w and side h) for a given diameter. Dimensions are for equal volume flow rate, in pascals per metre (Pa/m), and surface roughness as those for the selected circular duct although the velocity will be higher. Where velocity in the circular duct is near the limits of the table, an area-for-area calculation might be more appropriate.

Diagram 1 is a simplified version of table 4.40 to illustrate its use.

The diagram is divided. The top section gives the dimensions for sides w and h given at the top and right hand side for a rectangular duct, while the bottom section gives the dimensions for sides w and h given at the bottom and left hand side.

(See Design Watchpoint 1.)

Diagram 1

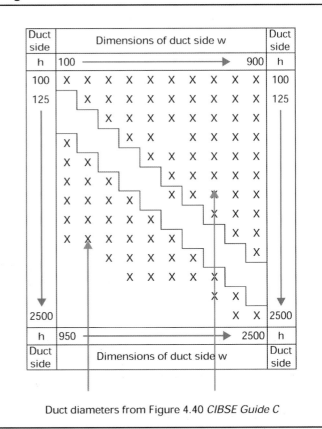

Duct diameters from Figure 4.40 *CIBSE Guide C*

Design Approach

The aspects that need to be considered are discussed in sheet A1 Duct sizing − general.

Key design inputs

- Duct diameters (mm) - The diameters for each section of the system being designed are required. These are found using the chart figure 4.2 *CIBSE Guide C* (see Sheet A2 for sizing procedure) or by calculation

(See Design Watchpoint 2.)

Design outputs

- A preliminary schedule of duct dimensions and lengths. These should be re-checked against client requirements, space available, aspect ratio requirements, and, availability, and changed as necessary. As experience is gained this can be done in one step but cross-checks should always be done at the final stage
- See also design outputs given under sheet A1 Duct sizing − general

A3   DUCT SIZING - CIRCULAR TO RECTANGULAR DUCT

Calculation procedure

Step 1. Preliminary dimensions – find the duct diameter on table 4.40 *CIBSE Guide C* and read off duct side w and duct side h. If the diameter is not on the chart take the nearest available size.

Step 2. Mark the dimensions, volume flow rate, velocity and pressure drop for each section on a drawing layout. This can be done as a cross-check (see sheet A1- Duct sizing – general).

Step 3. Re-check and change the dimensions as required to make sure that the aspect ratios are acceptable. Cross-check that the pressure drop and velocity values are still acceptable.

Step 4. Check that at each change of section only one dimension changes.

Example 1
For a duct diameter of 1100 mm find the equivalent rectangular dimensions using table 4.40. Use values of exactly 1100 mm (these will be found on the lower section of the table).

Diagram 2

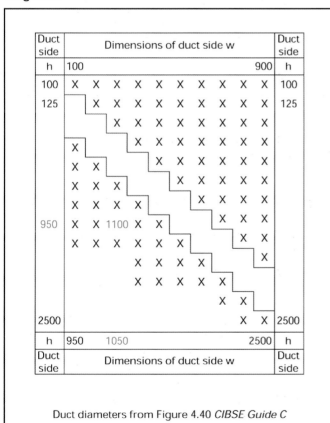

Duct diameters from Figure 4.40 *CIBSE Guide C*

Dimensions given are 1050 mm for side w, and 950 mm for side h.

Example 2
For a diameter of 200 mm find the equivalent rectangular dimensions using table 4.40:

Diagram 3

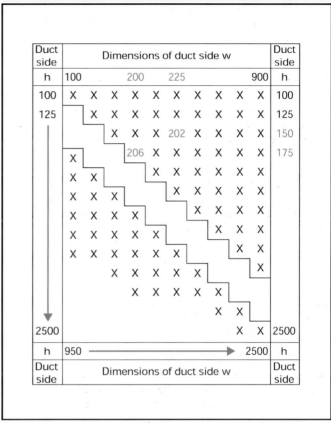

The exact dimension of 200 mm is not on table C4.40 but the 202 mm is on the table. This gives rectangular dimensions of 225 mm for side w, and 150 mm for side h. However, there may be constraints in plant space allowance such as the maximum allowable length of any one side is 200 mm. If this were the case then the dimensions selected above, given by the diameter of 202 mm, would not be feasible. If this were the case then another value would need to be used on the chart that is close to the original value of 200 mm. The chart does have a value for 206 mm, this gives dimensions of 200 mm for side w, and 175 mm for side h. This would satisfy the limits of the space allowance.

As a different diameter has been chosen, the designer should refer back to figure 4.2 *CIBSE Guide C* to check any differences in pressure drop and velocity that have occurred.

Example 3
Preliminary sizing
Using the duct diameters found in system 1 from the Duct Sizing – Selecting a duct size sheet A2 with a constant pressure-drop, find the equivalent rectangular duct using the exact diameters or the nearest value.

The diameters sized for system 1 from sheet A2 Duct sizing – Selecting a circular duct size, are shown in table 1.

© BSRIA BG 30/2003

A3   DUCT SIZING - CIRCULAR TO RECTANGULAR DUCT

Table I

These are the initial diameter sizes found using the *CIBSE* duct-sizing chart figure 4.2, with the relevant volume flow rate and maintaining a pressure drop of 1 Pa/m for each section.

Section	q m³/s	ΔP Pa/m	v m/s	Diameter mm
1	0·1	1	3·6	190
2	0·15	1	4	225
3	0·25	1	4·5	270
4	0·13	1	3·9	210
5	0·38	1	5·0	308
6	0·2	1	4·4	245
7	0·58	1	5·5	370

Step 1. Preliminary dimensions. Using table 4.40 from *CIBSE Guide C*, determine the preliminary rectangular duct dimensions from the diameters shown in table 1. If the diameter value does not appear on the chart, use the nearest value, in other words diameter 245 mm is not on the chart but 246 mm is. The preliminary dimensions are shown in table 2 with the corresponding diameter that was used, (ie 246 mm not 245 mm).

Table 2

Section	q m³/s	Diameter used on table 4.4, (exact or closest to diameters in table 1)	Preliminary dimensions mm w x h
1	0·1	190	200 x 150
2	0·15	225	350 x 125
3	0·25	269	350 x 175
4	0·13	211	400 x 100
5	0·38	308	350 x 225
6	0·2	246	250 x 200
7	0·58	371	600 x 200

Step 2. At this point the dimensions determined from table 4.40 *CIBSE Guide C*, should be put onto a layout drawing.

System I - Preliminary rectangular dimensions

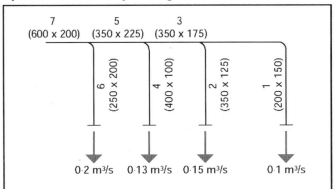

These dimensions will give 1 Pa/m (or as close to 1 Pa/m as is feasible), throughout the system. This is achieved because the duct diameters from figure 4.2 have been followed as closely as possible. Where a non exact diameter is used, for example 242 mm instead of 240 mm, this should be referred back to figure 4.2 to check what difference this makes to the pressure drop (Pa/m). If the difference in diameter is very small, as it is here, then the difference may be negligible, but this should always be checked.

(See Design Watchpoint 3.)

If the duct dimensions found in example 3 were to be used then the system would look something like the diagram below:

Diagram 4

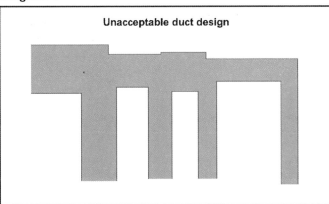

The diagram is not to scale, and of course, is only in 2D, but does give an idea of the result of using non-standard sizes and changing both dimensions of the duct at the same time when reducing (or enlarging). In practice only one side is changed at each volume flow difference and this would normally be to standard manufacturer's sizes (see sheet A1 Duct sizing – general). The pressure drops through each section would need to be checked to make sure that they are within acceptable limits for the type of system.

(See Design Watchpoint 4.)

➤ **Design tip:** Reducing the number of duct fittings, such as reductions and enlargements will reduce the overall cost.

➤ **Design tip:** when sizing a branch that is to feed a grille try to relate the aspect ratio to the grille dimensions; this may not always be a ratio of 1:1.

Step 3. The preliminary sets of rectangular dimensions are unacceptable They are uneconomic in terms of standard or readily available sizes, have more than one dimension changed at connecting sections, will have practically unachievable fittings and is generally a poor design so therefore must be reconsidered.

The designer should be aware of the acceptable limits for both pressure drop and velocity, and know of any physical constraints within the building that will affect the design. With this information the aspect ratio of the ducts (therefore dimensions) can be re-considered but only one dimension should be changed at a time.

A3 DUCT SIZING - CIRCULAR TO RECTANGULAR DUCT

The client's requirements are such that the volume flow rate must be maintained and the pressure drop should not exceed 1·0 Pa/m run. The velocity must not exceed 6 m/s. For this example the branches must have an aspect ratio of 1:1.

Once the acceptable limits of velocity, pressure loss, the desired aspect ratio, avoiding changing both dimensions of duct from joining sections and maintaining the required volume flow rate are known, the duct dimensions can be re-considered.

For example, Section 7 has preliminary rectangular dimensions of 600 mm x 200 mm (table 2) giving an aspect ratio of 3:1, determined from the initial equivalent circular duct diameter of 370 mm (table 1). A better choice would be to select the rectangular dimensions of 400 mm x 300 mm which has an equivalent diameter of 381 mm. This gives an aspect ratio of 4:3 (1:0·75), which is far closer to 1:1 than 3:1. Referring the equivalent diameter of 381 mm back to the *CIBSE* duct sizing chart figure 4.2, the velocity and pressure loss are also within the required limits.

Step 4. The next step is to reconsider the joining sections, remembering the client's requirements, aspect ratio and any factors that may determine parts of the design. There may be more than one option available - the choice is based on suitability and application.

Table 3

Section	ΔP Pa/m	v m/s	Equivalent diameter	Dimensions (mm) w x h
1	0·55	2·8	220	200 x 200
2	0·9	3·8	220	200 x 200
3	1	4·5	269	300 x 200
4	0·75	3·3	220	200 x 200
5	1	5·0	308	400 x 200
6	1	4·2	248	225 x 225
7	0·65	4·6	381	400 x 300

The new dimensions should be marked onto a layout drawing. If space permits then it would be useful to show all the information at each section in the form of a cross.

For example:

q	mm x mm		0·15	200 x 200
ΔP	v	→	0·9	3·8

System 1 Final dimensions

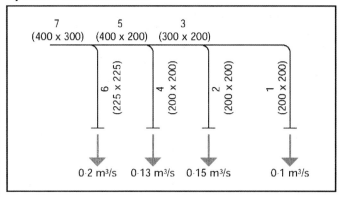

From the layout drawing of the final dimensions it can be seen that the dimensions of section 7 are 400 x 300 mm and the dimensions of the branch section 6 are 225 x 225 mm. Both dimensions have been changed, but the resultant dimensions have an aspect ratio of 1:1. If the requirements were not that the branches must have an aspect ratio of 1:1, other dimensions could have been used. This could have lead to the possibility of the volume flow rate being decreased. Decisions like this will frequently need to be made when designing a system. Having the criteria readily available along with advice from senior engineers will help junior engineers in making these decisions.

References
CIBSE Guide B3, *Ductwork*, Appendix 6, 2002, ISBN 1 903287 20 0
CIBSE Guide C, *Reference Data,* Section 4, 2001, ISBN 7506 5360 4
BSRIA, *Rules of Thumb,* TN 15/2001, BSRIA 2001, ISBN 086022 587 9
Lawrence Race G, *Design Checks for HVAC – A Quality Control Framework for Building Services Engineers* – sheets 27 and 45, AG 1/2002, BSRIA 2002, ISBN 0 86022 589 5
BSI, BS EN 1506:1998, *Ventilation for buildings – Sheet metal air ducts and fitting with circular cross section – Dimensions*. BSI 1998, ISBN 0580290247

See also:
Sheet A1 Duct sizing – General
Sheet A2 Duct sizing – Selecting a circular duct size
Sheet A4 Duct sizing – Pressure loss through fittings
Sheet A5 Duct system – Index run
Sheet A8 Air density correction

DESIGN WATCHPOINTS

1. When reading duct diameters from the chart figure 4.2, it may be that the exact diameter is not found on table 4.40. In this situation the nearest value from the original diameter value should be used. Always re-check the pressure drop as this varies even with small changes in the diameter.

2. Check the units and convert from metres to millimetres as table 4.40 *CIBSE Guide C* is in millimetres.

3. Pressure drops should always be checked. Even relatively small changes in diameter can cause substantial changes in pressure drop.

4. Using non-standard duct sizes can increase costs. However, there may be situations where using non-standard duct sizes is necessary due to restraints on the allocated space for the ductwork such as ceiling beams and riser shafts.

A4 DUCT SIZING – PRESSURE LOSS THROUGH FITTINGS

Overview

Pressure drops across fittings need to be determined in order to calculate the total pressure drop of the system in order to select a fan. The fitting pressure drop equals the fitting pressure loss factor times P_v

$$\Delta P = \zeta \times P_v = \zeta \times 0.5 \times \rho \times v^2$$

Where:
- ΔP = Fitting pressure drop (Pa)
- ζ = Pressure loss factor
- ρ = Density (kg/m^3)
- v = Velocity (m/s)
- P_v = $0.5 \times \rho \times v^2$ = velocity pressure

> **Design tip:** With air systems, the ductwork fittings lead to a high proportion of the total pressure losses through the system. This is not the case with pipework systems.

Design information required
(See sheet A1 – duct sizing – general)

System layout
Including types of duct, and the specific fittings used within the system.

Duct details
Full details of the duct are required in order to select the correct velocity pressure factor. For each fitting the information required (if appropriate) is:

- cross sectional area (m^2)
- dimensions (m)
- angles (°)
- velocities through each part (m/s)
- volume flow rates through each part (m^3/s)

Air density (kg/m^3)

Pressure loss factors (ζ)
(See Design Watchpoint 1.) For each duct fitting under consideration. These can be found in *CIBSE Guide C*, in tables 4.60 – 4.104 for rectangular fittings, tables 4.105 – 4.114 for rectangular to circular fittings (or vice versa), and tables 4.115 – 4.152 for circular components and fittings. Data is also available in ASHRAE and HVCA guidance.

Calculation procedure
To calculate the pressure loss through a fitting the following steps are required:

Step 1. Check the duct details for each part of the fitting and work out the ratios needed to select the pressure factor.

Step 2. Check the value for density used is correct for the conditions.

Step 3. Select the appropriate velocity pressure loss factor (ζ).

Step 4. Know the velocity in m/s of the air of the combined flow (if a tee).

Step 5. Apply these figures to:
$\Delta P = \zeta \times 0.5 \times \rho \times v^2$. (See Design Watchpoint 2.)

Example 1
Calculate the pressure loss through the fitting. This example uses the data from the branch and straight fitting comprising of sections 1,2 and 3. (See Design Watchpoint 3.)

Design data
Mitre bend with an angle of 90°
Velocity of 2.8 m/s
Density of 1.2 kg/m^3 (at 20°C, 43% sat.)
Dimensions – duct height (h) of 0.2 m and width (w) of 0.2 m.

The dimensions and velocities are that of the final choice of duct sizes for system 1, used in sheets A2 and A3.

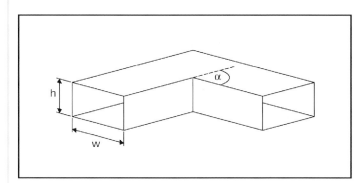

Step 1. Height h = 0.2 m, width w = 0.2 m, therefore h/w = 0.2/0.2 = 1 and angle α = 90°.

Step 2. Density = 1.2 kg/m^2, standard conditions apply.

Step 3. Select ζ from table 4.68, ζ = 1.19.

Step 4. There is only one velocity as the fitting is not a tee, therefore v = 2.8 m/s

Step 5. Apply to calculation:

$$\Delta P = \zeta \times 0.5 \times \rho \times v^2$$
$$\Delta P = 1.19 \times 0.5 \times 1.2 \times 7.84 = 5.6 \text{ Pa}$$

Example 2
Calculate the pressure loss through the fitting.

Design data
A 90° swept diverging rectangular duct branch.

Combined flow: Dimensions of combined flow, 0.3 m x 0.2 m
Cross sectional area of combined flow, A_c = 0.06 m^2,
Volume flow rate of combined flow q_c = 0.25 m^3/s
Velocity in the combined flow of v_c = 4.5 m/s

Straight flow: Dimensions of straight, 0.2 m x 0.2 m
Cross sectional area of the straight flow, A_s = 0.04 m^2,
Volume flow rate of straight flow q_s = 0.1 m^3/s
Velocity in the straight flow v_s = 2.8 m/s

Branch flow: Dimensions of branch, 0.2 m x 0.2 m
Cross sectional area of the branch flow, A_s = 0.04 m^2,
Volume flow rate of branch flow q_b = 0.15 m^3/s
Velocity in the branch flow v_b = 3.8 m/s

A4   DUCT SIZING – PRESSURE LOSS THROUGH FITTINGS

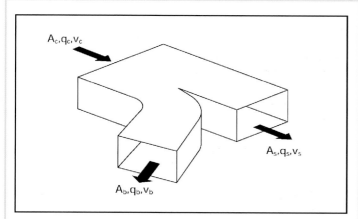

Note:

$q_c = q_s + q_b$,

$0.25 \text{ m}^3/\text{s} = 0.1 \text{ m}^3/\text{s} + 0.15 \text{ m}^3/\text{s}$.

Step 1. Duct details are given, the ratios required (see *CIBSE* table 4·99 and 4·100 *Guide C*) are:

$A_s/A_c = 0.04/0.06 = 0.66$

$A_b/A_c = 0.04/0.06 = 0.66$

$q_s/q_c = 0.1/0.25 = 0.4$

$q_b/q_c = 0.15/0.25 = 0.375$

Step 2. Density = 1·2 kg/m³, standard conditions apply.

Step 3. Two values of ζ are required one for the straight section and one for the branch.

To determine ζ from table 4.99 for the straight the ratios q_s/q_c, A_s/A_c and A_b/A_c are required. The value that is the closest to the ratios calculated is ζ_{c-s} equals 0·04.

To determine ζ from table 4.100 for the branch the ratios q_b/q_c, A_s/A_c and A_b/A_c are required.

The value that is the closest to the area ratios calculated is interpolated between 0·3 and 0·4 for q_b/q_c, is $\zeta_{c-b} = 0.305$.

Step 4. Velocity of the combined flow, $v_c = 4.5$ m/s.

Step 5. Therefore using:

$\Delta P = \zeta \times 0.5 \times \rho \times v^2$

For Straight:

$\Delta P = 0.04 \times 0.5 \times 1.2 \times 20.25 = 0.486$ Pa

For Branch:

$\Delta P = 0.305 \times 0.5 \times 1.2 \times 20.25 = 3.706$ Pa

References
CIBSE Guide B3, *Ductwork*, Appendix 6, 2002, ISBN 1 903287 20 0
CIBSE Guide C*, Reference Data*, Section 4, 2001, ISBN 7506 5360 4
BSRIA, *Rules of Thumb,* TN 15/2001, BSRIA 2001, ISBN 086022 587 9
Lawrence Race G, *Design Checks for HVAC – A Quality Control Framework for Building Services Engineers* – sheets 27 and 45, AG 1/2002, BSRIA 2002, ISBN 0 86022 589 5

See also:
Sheet A1 Duct sizing – General
Sheet A2 Duct sizing – Selecting a circular duct size
Sheet A3 Duct sizing – Circular to rectangular ducts
Sheet A5 Duct system – Index run
Sheet A7 Grille and diffuser sizing
Sheet A8 Air density correction

DESIGN WATCHPOINTS

1. Density varies with pressure and temperature; engineers should use a corrected figure if the building is at a high altitude or if heated or cooled air is being supplied.

2. As with pipework design, a common mistake is to apply ζ for a tee piece to the wrong part of the branch. The values of ζ in the new *CIBSE Guide C* should be used with the velocity pressure of the combined flow.

3. *CIBSE Guide C* refers to velocity as 'c'; when reading documents check the symbol definitions and suffixes as they may differ. These sheets use 'v' for velocity.

A5 DUCT SYSTEM – INDEX RUN

Overview

The index run within a system is the run that has the highest resistance to the flow of air and supplies the index terminal. In other words, the worst case possible when considering pressure losses within a system. It is usually, (but not always), the longest run in the system. Sometimes a shorter run with a greater number of fitting or items of equipment can be the index run.

The index pd (pressure drop) is required in order to successfully size the fan for the system. If the fan can work to the pressure demands of the index run, then all other runs will work.

To identify the index run the pressure drop for several runs may need to be found. The pressure drop across each length of duct, fittings and grille/diffuser within these runs will need to be calculated to determine the total pressure drop for each run. The one with the largest pressure drop will be the index run. (See Design Watchpoint 1.)

If the system only consists of one run then the pressure loss through that run is used to size the fan.

> ➤ **Design tip:** If a packaged air handling unit is used then this would include the fan(s). In such cases the manufacturer of the packaged air handling unit will select the fan but will need to know the external pressure loss (pressure losses in ductwork external to the packaged unit).

Design information required
(See also sheet A1 – duct sizing – general)

Number of runs
Each run within a multi-run system needs to be clearly identified.

Section details
Each section of the system needs to be clearly identified with details of all the components in that section. The sections make up the runs, so care is required when deciding which component should be in which section.

Duct sizing details
All ductwork and fittings should have been sized with pascals per metre run and ζ values for all fittings and components. Data is available from tables such as those found in *CIBSE Guide C*.

Air handling unit and equipment details
If a packaged air handling unit is to be used the pressure drop through it may not be known at this time but a reasonable allowance must be made (and checked later) for this and any other equipment for which details are not available such as heating/cooling batteries, filters, humidifiers, and specific fan power in watts per litre per second (W/ls^{-1}).

Key design inputs
- Length of each section (m)
- Pressure drop per unit length for each section (Pa/m)
- Velocities through all branches and tees (m/s)

Calculation procedure

Step 1. Identify and assign a reference to each section. For example number each length of duct, identify each fitting, where branches are used identify each path of the branch by different references or by using the corresponding duct length identities. For example, as shown below, the ductwork leading to the branch section 1, the ductwork that branches off (branch) section 2 and, the ductwork after the branch but still in line with the combined flow (straight) section 3.

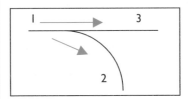

Once the ductwork has been labelled for each section the branch needs to be referenced. The branch fitting consists of two parts, the straight and the branched. The pressure loss for each part will need to be calculated separately as the pressure loss factor (ζ) for the straight length and the branch is often different.

The parts of the branch fitting can be identified as:
Branch ref: 1-3, for the straight part and,
Branch ref: 1-2, for the branched part.

When calculating the total pressure drop in a section, identifying the fittings such as branches or similar fittings needs to be done correctly. In the example above the pressure loss across branch reference: 1-3 should be included in the total pressure loss for section 3. Section 3 starts from this part of the branch. The airflow that is diverted to section 2 includes the pressure loss for branch reference: 1-2 as the air has to pass this point to get to section 2. It is important to identify each fitting and total straight lengths within a section as this makes it easier to identify each run.

Step 2. Identify each run by the sections it consists of, for example run A equals 1,3, run B equals 1,2. These sections should already include the fittings that apply to individual runs such as elbows and enlargements, but also the part of any branch that applies to the run.

Step 3. Calculate all direct pressure losses across fittings and ductwork in each section, for fittings $\Delta P = \zeta \times 0.5 \times \rho \times v^2$, for straight duct lengths use pascals per metre times length in metres. (See sheets A2, A3 and A4)

Step 4. Add up the total pressure losses from each section within a run to give a run pressure drop.

Step 5. Identify the index run from analysis of the various pressure drops of each run, in other words the highest pressure drop. (See Design Watchpoint 3.)

> ➤ **Design tip:** The resistance in the air handling unit is common to all runs.

> ➤ **Design tip:** Include allowance for lift where applicable (as done in pumps serving high level water tanks). A duct extracting air from atmosphere at ground level and discharging at the roof of a 10 storey building would have to provide about 420 Pa lift (12 Pa/m).

A5 DUCT SYSTEM – INDEX RUN

Example

Calculate the index run for system 1 using the sizes shown below. (Figures for duct diameters are from sheet A2 *Duct sizing - Selecting a circular duct size – the constant pressure drop method*, the equivalent rectangular dimensions are from sheet A3 *Duct Sizing - Circular to rectangular ducts*, Example 3.) In order to keep the worked example simplified, this example does not contain all the fittings such as dampers that would normally be required in a ducting system. *CIBSE Guide B3*, Appendix A6 contains a more detailed worked example of ductwork sizing and pressure drop calculations.

Step 1. Identify the different sections and their design details.

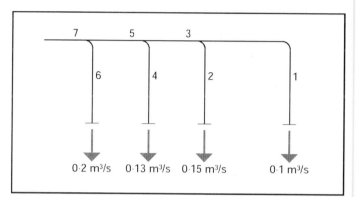

Design data

AHU pressure drop = 150 pa

Section details

Section 1

Diameter = 220 mm,
Equivalent rectangular dimensions: w = 200 mm x h = 200 mm
Straight Ductwork, 6 m + 8 m equals 14 m length,
1 x elbow, mitre, rectangular (angle 90°)
Branch ref: 3-1,
Discharge to space,
1 velocity head at discharge.
Velocity = 2·8 m/s
$\Delta P/l = 0·55$ Pa/m

Section 2

Diameter = 220 mm,
Equivalent rectangular dimensions: w = 220 mm x h = 200 mm
Straight Ductwork, 6 m
Branch ref: 3-2,
Discharge to space (plane extract),
1 velocity head at discharge.
Velocity = 3·8 m/s
$\Delta P/l = 0·9$ Pa/m

Section 3

Diameter = 269 mm,
Equivalent rectangular dimensions: w = 300 mm x h = 200 mm
Straight ductwork, 5 m
Branch ref: 5-3,
Velocity = 4·5 m/s
$\Delta P/l = 1$ Pa/m

Section 4

Diameter = 220 mm,
Equivalent rectangular dimensions: w = 200 mm x h = 200 mm
Straight ductwork, 6 m
Branch ref: 5-4,
Discharge to space (plane extract),
1 velocity head at discharge.
Velocity = 3·3 m/s
$\Delta P/l = 0·75$ Pa/m

Section 5

Diameter = 308 mm,
Equivalent rectangular dimensions: w = 400 mm x h = 200 mm
Straight ductwork, 5 m
Branch ref: 7-5
Velocity = 5 m/s
$\Delta P/l = 1$ Pa/m

Section 6

Diameter = 248 mm,
Equivalent rectangular dimensions: w = 225 mm x h = 225 mm
Straight ductwork, 6 m
Branch ref: 7-6,
Discharge to space (plane extract),
1 velocity head at discharge.
Velocity = 4·2 m/s
$\Delta P/l = 1·0$ Pa/m

Section 7

Diameter = 381 mm,
Equivalent rectangular dimensions: w = 400 mm x h = 300 mm
Straight ductwork, 5 m
Velocity = 4·6 m/s
$\Delta P/l = 0·65$ Pa/m

Don't forget the ductwork leading to the AHU, ie the fresh air intake which may include louvers or other restrictions to the airflow.

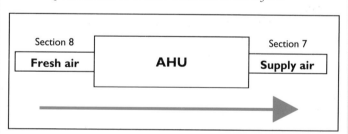

Section 8 (Same as 7)

Diameter equals 381 mm, equivalent rectangular dimensions:
w = 400 mm x h = 300 mm
Straight ductwork, 5 m,
Air entry at fresh air intake (plane duct entry),
Velocity = 4·6 m/s
$\Delta P/l = 1·0$ Pa/m

Note that for plain extract and duct entries engineers should assume a mesh with 50% free area (CIBSE Guide C Section 4.10.5.19 table 4.150)

Step 2. Identify each run by the sections:

Circuit A: 8,7,6
Circuit B: 8,7,5,4
Circuit C: 8,7,5,3,2
Circuit D: 8,7,5,3,1

A5 DUCT SYSTEM – INDEX RUN

Step 3. Calculate pressure loss through each section. See Index run tables sections 1–8 below and opposite page.

Step 4. Total pressure loss in each run:

Circuit A: 30·56 + 3·25 +48·58= 82·39 Pa
Circuit B: 30·56 + 3·25 +4·54 + 33·01= 71·36 Pa
Circuit C: 30·56 + 3·25 + 4·54 + 4·46 + 40·72 = 83·53 Pa
Circuit D: 30·56+3·25+4·54+4·46+30·94 = 73·75 Pa

Step 5. Circuit C is the index run with a pressure loss of 83·5 Pa. Adding the resistance of the AHU of 150 Pa gives a total system pressure drop of 233·5 Pa.

> **Design tip:** Often up to two thirds of the system pressure drop of ductwork systems occurs in the AHU.

Index run tables sections 1-8
Where:
V = Volume flow rate m^3/s
D = Diameter in mm from figure 4.2
w x h = equivalent rectangular dimensions, sides w and h (mm)
A = area in m^2
Pa/m=pressure loss per metre from figure 4.2
L = Length of straight duct (m)
ζ = pressure loss factor
v = velocity (m/s)
Pv = velocity pressure, (0·5 x ρ x v^2, always use for combined flow where branches/tees are used)
ΔP =pressure loss in duct or fitting

References
CIBSE Guide B3, *Ductwork*, Appendix 6, 2002, ISBN 1 903287 20 0
CIBSE Guide C, *Reference Data*, Section 4, 2001, ISBN 7506 5360 4
BSRIA, *Rules of Thumb*, TN 15/2001, BSRIA 2001, ISBN 086022 587 9
Lawrence Race G, *Design Checks for HVAC – A Quality Control Framework for Building Services Engineers* – sheets 27 and 45, AG 1/2002, BSRIA 2002, ISBN 0 86022 589 5

See also:
Sheet C4 Ventilation – Fresh air requirements
Sheet A1 Duct sizing – General
Sheet A2 Duct sizing – Selecting a circular duct size
Sheet A3 Duct sizing – Circular to rectangular ducts
Sheet A4 Duct system – Pressure loss through fittings
Sheet A6 Fan sizing

DESIGN WATCHPOINTS

1. Engineers should not forget that the run will need to include any heating/cooling batteries, fan connections and any other related fittings and equipment.
2. Often the longest run is the index run, but there is always the possibility of a shorter run with many fittings being the index run.
3. Engineers should include ductwork prior to the fan, the air discharge and air intake and any grilles, diffusers or meshes.
4. Remember to add the resistance of the AHU, or separate plant items if a non-packaged unit is used, to obtain the overall system pressure drop to use in fan sizing.

Section 1

Fitting	V m^3/s	D mm	w x h mm	Area m^2	Pa/m	L m	ζ	v	Pv	ΔP
Straight length	0·1	220	200x200	0·04	0·55	14		2·8		7·7
Elbow @ 90°							1·19	2·8	4·70	5·59
Branch Ref:3-1							0·04	4·5	12·15	0·49
Discharge to space							2·65	2·8	4·70	12·46
1 Velocity head								2·8	4·70	4·70
Total ΔP										30·94

Section 2

Fitting	V m^3/s	D mm	w x h mm	Area m^2	Pa/m	L m	ζ	v	Pv	ΔP
Straight length	0·15	220	200x200	0·04	0·9	6		3·8		5·40
Branch Ref:3-2							0·305	4·5	12·15	3·71
Discharge to space							2·65	3·8	8·66	22·95
1 Velocity head								3·8	8·66	8·66
Total ΔP										40·72

A5 DUCT SYSTEM – INDEX RUN

Section 3

Fitting	V m³/s	D mm	w x h mm	Area m²	Pa/m	L m	ζ	v	Pv	ΔP
Straight length	0·25	269	300x200	0·06	1	5		4·5		5
Branch Ref:5-3							-0·036	5·0	15	-0·54
Total ΔP										4·46

Section 4

Fitting	V m³/s	D mm	w x h mm	Area m²	Pa/m	L m	ζ	v	Pv	ΔP
Straight length	0·13	220	200x200	0·04	0·75	6		3·3		4·5
Branch Ref:5-4							0·312	5·0	15	4·68
Discharge to space							2·65	3·3	6·53	17·30
1 Velocity head								3·3	6·53	6·53
Total ΔP										33·01

Section 5

Fitting	V m³/s	D mm	w x h mm	Area m²	Pa/m	L m	ζ	v	Pv	ΔP
Straight length	0·38	308	40x200	0·08	1	5		5·0		5
Branch Ref:7-5							-0·036	4·6	12·70	-0·46
Total ΔP										4·54

Section 6

Fitting	V m³/s	D mm	w x h mm	Area m²	Pa/m	L m	ζ	v	Pv	ΔP
Straight length	0·2	248	225x225	0·0625	1·0	6		4·2		6·0
Branch Ref:7-6							0·312	4·6	12·70	3·96
Discharge to space							2·65	4·2	10·58	28·04
1 Velocity head								4·2	10·58	10·58
Total ΔP										48·58

Section 7

Fitting	V m³/s	D mm	w x h mm	Area m²	Pa/m	L m	ζ	v	Pv	ΔP
Straight length	0·58	381	400x300	0·12	0·65	5		4·6		3·25
Total ΔP										3·25

Section 8

Fitting	V m³/s	D mm	w x h mm	Area m²	Pa/m	L m	ζ	v	Pv	ΔP
Straight length	0·58	381	400x300	0·12	0·65	5		4·6		3·25
Fresh air intake							2·15	4·6	12·70	27·31
Total ΔP										30·56

© BSRIA BG 30/2003

A6   FAN SIZING

Overview

There are two main categories of fan: axial and centrifugal. The difference between the two is the way in which the air passes through the fan.

Axial fans are in line with the airflow. They are mainly used in low pressure, high volume applications with efficiencies in the 60 to 75% range. Noise can be a problem.

Centrifugal fans resemble a construction similar to a water wheel. The air enters in line with the drive shaft and exits at 90° to the entering air.

Centrifugal fans are the most commonly used in air conditioning systems for medium to high pressure applications, with efficiencies in the 50 to 85% range.

There are different types of centrifugal fans determined by the type of blade and configuration. The following describes the two most common types.

Forward curved fan (multivane)

Many small blades mounted with the tips, inclined to the direction of rotation. Commonly used as they can move the largest volume of air for the fan and are quiet. They do have a severely rising power characteristic.

Backward curved fans

Tips of blades mounted at an incline away from the direction of rotation. Normally the impeller is fitted with 10 or 16 blades. These fans are not as compact as forward-curved fans but are more efficient and have a non-overloading characteristic. They are used in systems where a high or varying pressure is needed.

Further information is available in *CIBSE Guide B2*, section 5.11, table 5.17 gives a summary of nine fan types with typical efficiencies and applications.

Fan laws

For a given system;

$$Q \propto N$$
$$P \propto N^2$$
$$W \propto N^3$$
$$P \propto \rho$$
$$W \propto \rho$$
$$Q \propto D^3$$
$$P \propto D^2$$
$$W \propto D^5$$

Where:
Q = volume flow rate
N = speed
P = pressure developed
W = power
D = diameter of the impeller
ρ = density

The fundamental fluid flow laws can be found in various sources ranging from guides such as *CIBSE Guide B2*, section 5.11, to text books such as *Woods Practical Guide* to *Fan Engineering*.

> **Design tip**: Manufacturers determine a fan's performance by testing and application of fan laws, and will present the data typically in the form of charts of pressure versus volume flow rate.

Fan Characteristic

Fan sizing follows the same rules as pump sizing (see W5).

The fan supplies energy to the air stream which replaces the energy lost due to friction. The energy supplied by the fan is measured in terms of pressure (energy per unit volume) just as the energy lost due to friction is measured in terms of pressure loss. Fan sizing involves selecting a fan which will provide just enough pressure energy to produce the design air flow rate. Over-sizing the fan will inject more energy than necessary into the air stream resulting in excessive flow rate or the need to add additional resistance during balancing to absorb this energy. Energy is also wasted.

The pressure produced by a fan depends upon the volume flow rate of air which in turn depends upon the resistance of the ductwork. So, in order to select a fan, the pressure/volume characteristic of both fan and ductwork needs to be known.

Fan characteristics vary depending upon fan design, (centrifugal, axial etc); fan size and fan speed. This information is usually given in the form of data in graphs from the manufacturer.

The ductwork system characteristic follows a quadratic law:

$$\Delta P = RQ^2$$

Where:
ΔP = pressure loss
Q   = volume flow rate
R   = constant of proportionality

R is found from the calculated pressure loss at design flow rate (duct sizing).

As the pressure (energy per unit volume) developed by the fan will be completely absorbed by the air stream and consumed by friction, the only possible operating point is when $P=\Delta P$. This can be seen on graph 1:

A6 FAN SIZING

Graph 1

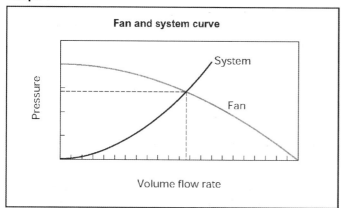

Fan and system curve

Graph 2

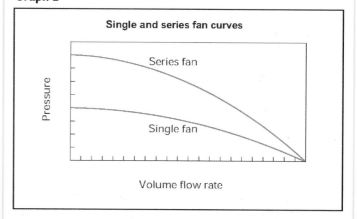

Single and series fan curves

Total, static and velocity pressure

Fan total pressure equals fan static pressure plus fan velocity pressure

In theory, the fan total pressure is available but much of this can be lost at the fan exit (and entry) which will not have been allowed for in the duct sizing calculations. It is usual therefore to select the fan on fan static pressure rather than fan total pressure.

Fan static pressure is the measured pressure difference between the fan inlet and the fan outlet.

Fan static pressure $= P_{tf} - P_v$
Where:

$P_{tf} =$ fan total pressure (Pa)

$P_v =$ fan velocity pressure at outlet

Fan speed

Reducing fan speed dramatically reduces power consumption, (see fan laws), and so is an excellent way of both regulating and controlling volume flow rate. (see - Variable Flow Control, General Information Report 41, BRECSU, 1996). The fan characteristic at any speed can be determined from its characteristic equation at full speed.

Dual fans

Sometimes dual fans are used either in series or parallel.

When comparing the fan characteristics of a single fan and dual fans in series (all identical) the pressure is doubled for a given volume flow rate.

When the system curve is plotted on the same graph the new operating point can be determined and compared with that of a single fan.

Graph 3

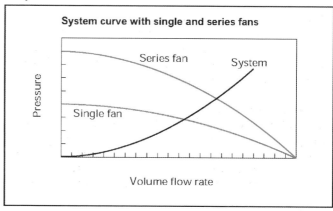

System curve with single and series fans

The same applies with parallel fans where the volume flow rate is doubled for a given pressure.

Graph 4

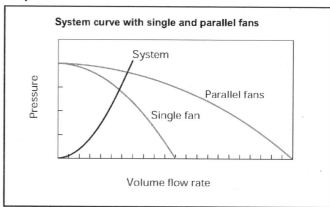

System curve with single and parallel fans

A6   FAN SIZING

Calculation procedure

Step 1. If not already available, calculate the ductwork index run pressure-drop and total system flow rate.

Step 2. Determine system equations for constant R. This can be done by substituting the required ΔP and Q into the equation $\Delta P = RQ^2$ and then solving for R.

Step 3. Select a fan that appears to operate within the required parameters and plot the system and fan characteristics on the same graph.

Step 4. Determine the operating point. Identify the operating pressure and flow rate.

Step 5. If there is a mismatch (for example the flow rate is too high), then either select another fan or change the fan output by either varying the speed (if necessary obtain new fan data and re-draw the graph) or restrict the flow by means of a damper.

Step 6. If a damper is required, calculate the pressure drop needed to achieve the system requirements.

Example

Step 1. A system has a volume flow rate requirement of 2 m^3/s with an index run ΔP of 100 Pa. Find an appropriate fan.

Pressure drop and volume flow rate are available in the units required.

Step 2. The constant R in the system characteristic curve equation can be calculated as show below:

$$\Delta P = RQ^2$$
Index run pd = 100Pa
Volume flow rate = 2 l/s
$$100 = R \times 2^2$$
ie $R = \dfrac{100}{4} = 25$
$$\Delta P = 25Q^2$$

Step 3. A fan needs to be selected that will work within the parameters of pressure and volume flow rate already stated. Selection will also depend on the type of system and design features of the fan. (See Design Watchpoint 1.)

Once a fan has been selected that can work in the range required, the fan and system curve should be plotted on a single graph. Some manufacturers will provide a range of fan curves already on a graph with efficiency and power curves underneath. If this is the case then the system curve can be drawn directly onto the graph and the operating points identified quickly. For this example it is assumed that the fan data is given in table form:

For a centrifugal fan operating at 15 rev/s:

FTP = fan total pressure (Pa)
Q = volume flow (l/s)

ftp	197·5	190	177·5	160	137·5	110	77·5
Q	0·5	1	1·5	2	2·5	3	3·5

This can be plotted in a graph of pressure against volume flow rate.

With the system curve also plotted the intersection point can also be found.

Graph 5

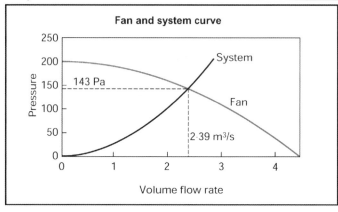

Step 4. The operating point occurs when the two curves intersect, 2·39 m^3/s at 143 Pa.

Step 5. As 2·39 m^3/s is too high, the fan will need to be either slowed down or restricted in order to achieve the required flow rate. Alternatively, a different fan may give a closer value; this is worth considering when comparing the efficiency of different fans at different speeds and pressures.

Step 6. If a damper were to be installed, what would the pressure drop be in order to achieve the requirements of the system?

Using 2·0 m^3/s determine the ΔP of the fan from the graph:

$$\Delta P = 160 \text{ Pa}$$

The fan is therefore developing more pressure than is required by the system. In order to match the fan to the system either the system characteristics must change (for example by adding a damper) or the fan characteristics must change (for example by changing the fan speed).

The pressure drop required in the ducting is 100 Pa. Here a damper has been added therefore the pressure drop across the damper would need to be:

$$160 \text{ Pa} - 100 \text{ Pa} = 60 \text{ Pa}$$

The pressure drop required over the damper adds 60% to the system resistance that is effectively wasted energy ie the fan develops 160 Pa, 60 Pa of which are absorbed by the damper.

A6 FAN SIZING

Alternatively the speed of the fan can be reduced to match the required volume flow rate.

By using the fan law $Q \propto N$:

$$\frac{Q}{Q}_{des} = \frac{N}{N}_{des}$$

Where:

Q_{des} = desired volume flow rate

N_{des} = desired fan rotational speed

The required speed can be determined that is needed to provide $2 \text{ m}^3/\text{s}$.

Therefore:

$$N_{des} = \frac{2}{2 \cdot 39} \times 15 = 12 \cdot 5 \, \text{rev/s}$$

This can also be achieved by using the fan law:

$P \propto N^2$:

$$\frac{P_{des}}{P} = \frac{N_{des}^2}{N^2}$$

Therefore:

$$N_{des}^2 = \frac{100}{143} \times 15^2 = 157 \cdot 3$$

$$N_{des} = \sqrt{157 \cdot 3} = 12 \cdot 5 \, \text{rev/s}$$

➢ **Design tip:** Always review the pressure required if a damper is used to match fan and system and consider other approaches as required for example speed control, change of fan, or use of a variable speed fan etc.

➢ **Design tip:** Using a damper to reduce the output is inefficient as it wastes fan energy. Varying the speed is preferred.

References

CIBSE Guide B2, *Ventilation and Air Conditioning*, Section 5.11, 2001, ISBN 1 903287 16 2

CIBSE TM30, *Improved Life Cycle Performance of Mechanical Ventilation Systems*, 2003, ISBN 1 903287 36 7

Daley, BB, *Woods Practical Guide to Fan Engineering*

Lawrence Race G, *Design Checks for HVAC – A Quality Control Framework for Building Services Engineers* – sheet 48, AG 1/2002, BSRIA 2002, ISBN 0 86022 589 5

See also:

Sheet A1 Duct sizing – General
Sheet A2 Duct sizing – Selecting a circular duct size
Sheet A3 Duct sizing – Circular to rectangular ducts
Sheet A4 Duct Sizing – Pressure loss through fittings
Sheet A5 Duct System – Index run

DESIGN WATCHPOINTS

1. When selecting the fan from fan curve charts, it is important to consider the efficiency of the fan. The fan efficiency curve is often on the same chart or sheet. If the fan selected satisfies the duty and pressure requirements but the efficiency is very low, a better choice would be to select a different fan with better efficiency but still meeting the requirements for the system.

2. It is worthwhile reading though all the manufacturer's data before starting. Correction factors provided by manufacturer's may be appropriate to specific ranges of products.

3. Don't forget the fan power output will be different from the power input (motor power). The overall efficiency of the motor and drive losses will be required to calculate this.

4. Consideration of system energy efficiency is now required under *Building Regulations Part L*. Specific fan power is an overall measure of the energy efficiency of the ventilation system – for a discussion of this see Section 2.1 of *CIBSE TM 30 - Improved life cycle performance of mechanical ventilation systems*.

5. Check that specific fan power does not exceed *Building Regulation requirements Part L* of 2W/l/s for systems in new buildings and 3W/l/s for new or refurbished systems installed in existing buildings.

A7   GRILLE AND DIFFUSER SIZING

Overview
In air conditioning and ventilation systems, the supply air needs to be introduced into the space effectively to enable the air to achieve the required cooling or heating.

Air terminal devices
All devices used to introduce air into the space are called air terminal devices, of which grilles and diffusers are the most common examples.

Although the terms grilles and diffusers are often used generically, the two types of air terminal devices are designed to introduce air in subtly different ways.

These devices come in many forms.

Grilles
This type of air terminal device discharges the air in a three-dimensional stream, normally perpendicular or nearly perpendicular to its face. Examples are:

- Single and double deflection
- Fixed bar
- Egg crate
- Non-vision
- Perforated stamped or mesh

Diffusers
Diffusers generally discharge air to make use of the coanda or ceiling effect, where the air stream sticks to the ceiling on leaving the device. An exception to this is the swirl diffuser, which generates a highly turbulent swirl effect on discharge, which enables very high air volumes to be supplied. Diffuser options include:

- Multi-cone
- Louvred face
- Perforated plate
- Slot
- Multi-blade
- Swirl

Other more specialist devices include:

- Nozzles/drums
- Disc valves
- Supply luminaires
- Ventilated ceilings
- Laminar flow panels
- Displacement ventilation diffusers

Design information required
Volume flow rate
The required volume flow rate for each space - the amount of air the grille or diffuser needs to handle will determine the size of diffuser or grille.

Internal design conditions
The required design condition in the space.

Supply air condition
The required supply air temperature and humidity to meet the heating and cooling requirement. Together with the other design information this will allow prediction of air diffusion patterns from the selected output.

> **Design tip:** For air conditioning systems diffuser and grille performance will need to be assessed under both heating and cooling modes.

Noise levels
The acceptable noise level for the space has a great effect on grille and diffuser sizing. Generally the more air that passes through a device, the higher the noise level.

Throw
The throw is the distance that the device pushes or throws the air. If the throw is too great, then excess velocities will create draughts. Conversely, too short a throw will result in poor air distribution.

Use of space
To determine limiting acceptable velocities in occupied zone etc.

Room characteristics
The room characteristics need to be evaluated so that issues such as available throw, possible device locations, occupancy patterns and locations can all be determined, and the equipment selected accordingly.

Sizing nomogram
The manufacturer will produce a nomogram for each grille or diffuser model to enable accurate sizing.

Design outputs
1. System design drawings showing diffuser positions, required supply air flow rates, throws and throw directions
2. Diffuser schedule including pressure drop, air volume flow rates, NR rating, details of plenum box, neck size/nominal face size. Method of support and finish

A7 GRILLE AND DIFFUSER SIZING

Calculation procedure

Most air terminal devices are sized using charts or data provided by the various equipment manufacturers, produced to accurately reflect the performance of their particular products.

The approach varies slightly depending on the type of air terminal device being considered, but a general method is described below.

Note: This procedure has been based on a nomogram produced by a particular manufacturer, and may differ from those produced by other companies. However, the same general principles will apply. Simplified drawings of the charts used are also shown.

Step 1. First, determine the volume flow rate to be handled by each outlet/device. The number of outlets will be chosen by a combination of total flow rate, size of room, coverage, available space, and the capacity of the device. This will be very specific to each case.

Step 2. Select the type of device necessary to give the required air flow pattern. This can be done from manufacturer's data. If there are a number of suitable options, other considerations such as aesthetics or device capacity may determine which type to use.

Step 3. Calculate the available throw for the device. To prevent excess velocity or over-blow, a rule of thumb is that this should be 75% of the distance from the device outlet to the opposite wall or, if there is another device in the facing wall, this should be 33% of the distance between them.

Step 4. Establish the maximum acceptable noise level.

Step 5. From the manufacturer's data, select the appropriate sizing nomogram for the device type being considered.

Step 6. Plot the required volume flow rate on the vertical scale on the left of the nomogram.

Step 7. Draw a line from the selected volume flow rate through the throw point on the next vertical line to the right hand side of the nomogram. This will now also indicate:

- a sound level
- jet velocity
- device pressure drop
- a point on the pivot line.

Step 8. Assuming that the sound level, jet velocity and pressure drop are acceptable, the device width and length can be found by striking a line through these two vertical lines, pivoting about the pivot point, until a suitable arrangement is found.

Step 9. For adjustable deflection grilles, a second chart must be referred to, in order to make sure that the air stream is at an acceptably low velocity by the time it enters the occupied zone. Referring to the drop chart, plot a line between the velocity value on the jet velocity vertical line and the throw distance on the throw vertical line. The jet velocity is read from the nomogram.

Step 10. From the other scale on this line read off the drop due to spread distance.

Step 11. Plot a line from the appropriate temperature differential value through the pivot point found from step 9 to the drop due to temperature differential line.

Step 12. Add together the two distances found in steps 10 and 11, and then subtract this value from the grille mounting height to find the height at which the acceptable air stream velocity occurs.

Step 13. Should this be greater than the distance between the top of the occupied zone and the grille, the blades will have to be adjusted accordingly.

Step 14. By reference to the manufacturer's spread nomogram, determine the amount or angle of deflection required. Reading the 0^0 deflection curve where it crosses the throw point value on the horizontal scale gives a spread drop distance. Adding this to the total drop found in step 12 above, gives the overall distance that the deflection must overcome.

Step 15. The maximum deflection permissible to achieve a comfortable air velocity in the occupied zone. Therefore, the blades must be deflected to achieve the following degree of deflection.

Step 16. The level of deflection indicated by the spread nomogram is found by interpolation between the distances plotted at $22 \cdot 5^0$ and 45^0.

Example

Size a suitable grille for the following office:

Design data

Room dimensions:		length	6 m
		width	3 m
		height	3 m
Air volume flow rate:			0·07 m³/s
Cooling temperature differential:			6°C
Acceptable noise level:			30 dbA
Grille mounting height:			2·75 m
Grille location:			centred in the 3 m wall

Step 1. and Step 2. Volume flow rate is given in the design criteria. For the application above, a single adjustable deflection grille has been selected.

Step 3. The throw will be equal to:

75% x distance from outlet to opposite wall
0·75 x 6
4·5 m

Step 4. The maximum acceptable sound pressure level as stated in the design criteria is 30 dbA.

A7 GRILLE AND DIFFUSER SIZING

A diagram of a sizing nomogram is shown below. The scales have not been included as this will depend on the nomogram used. References of A to I have been shown on the diagram to indicate the technical data with a legend below.

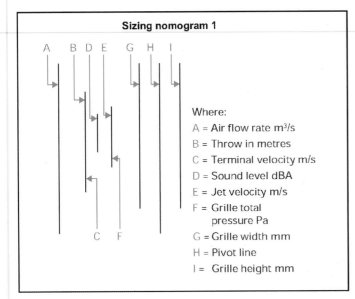

Where:
A = Air flow rate m³/s
B = Throw in metres
C = Terminal velocity m/s
D = Sound level dBA
E = Jet velocity m/s
F = Grille total pressure Pa
G = Grille width mm
H = Pivot line
I = Grille height mm

Step 5. and Step 6. Plot the required volume flow rate on the appropriate scale on the nomogram (diagram 2).

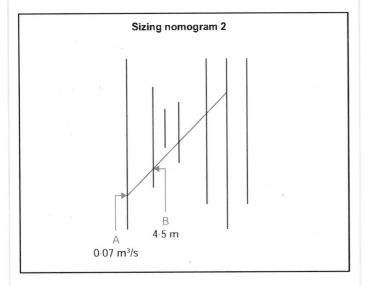

Step 7. Draw a line from the selected volume flow rate through the throw point on the appropriate line, (diagram 2), and across to the right hand side of the nomogram. This indicates the following data (diagram 3):

- sound level is below 20 dbA
- jet velocity is 1·9 m/s
- pressure drop is 2 Pa

These all meet the design criteria.

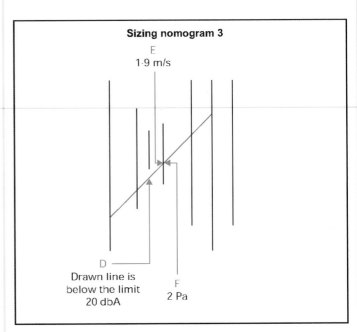

Step 8. By rotating about the pivot point, a grille size of 300 mm by 150 mm has been selected.

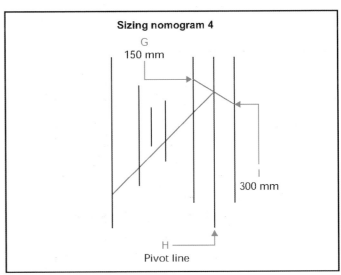

Step 9. and Step 10. Referring to the drop chart, plot a line between the velocity value on the jet velocity vertical line and the throw distance on the throw vertical line. The jet velocity is read from the nomogram as detailed in Step 7 above. The drop due to spread value is read off the scale as 0·54 m.

Step 11. Taking a point from the 6°C value on the temperature differential scale, and crossing through the pivot line at the point crossed in Step 9 and 10 above, and on to the drop due to temperature difference line. The value read here is 1·02 m.

Step 12. and Step13. This gives a combined drop distance of 1·56 m, (1·02 m + 0·54 m). This means that the air stream drops to: 2·75 m − 1·56 m = 1·19 m before an acceptable air stream velocity is achieved. As this is within the occupied zone, (2 m above floor level) this is not acceptable and therefore the spread chart will need to be used. If it were acceptable then the deflection would not be required.

A7 GRILLE AND DIFFUSER SIZING

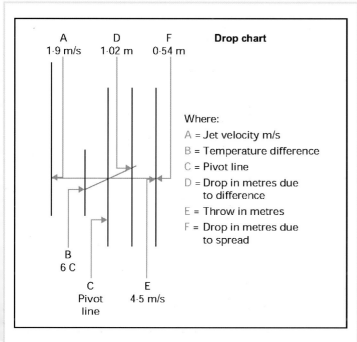

Drop chart

Where:
A = Jet velocity m/s
B = Temperature difference
C = Pivot line
D = Drop in metres due to difference
E = Throw in metres
F = Drop in metres due to spread

A
1·9 m/s

D
1·02 m

F
0·54 m

B
6 C

C
Pivot line

E
4·5 m/s

Step 14. From the manufacturer's spread chart, reading the 0^0 deflection curve where it crosses the throw point read from the horizontal scale gives a deflection of 1·6 m. Added to the total drop found in Steps 12 and 13 above results in a total drop of 3·16 m. Therefore, the blades must be adjusted to overcome this drop.

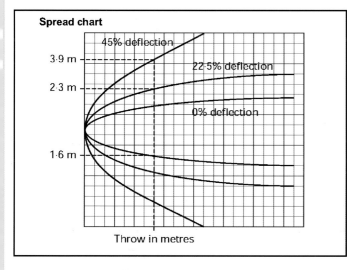

Spread chart

45% deflection
22·5% deflection
0% deflection

3·9 m
2·3 m
1·6 m

Throw in metres

Step 15. The maximum deflection permissible to achieve a comfortable air velocity in the occupied zone is

$$2·75 \text{ m} - 2·0 \text{ m} = 0·75 \text{ m}$$

Therefore, the blades must be deflected to achieve the following degree of deflection:

$$3·16 \text{ m} - 0·75 \text{ m} = 2·41 \text{ m}$$

Step 16. The level of deflection indicated by the spread nomogram, for this example is $23·9^0$, found by interpolation between the distances plotted at $22·5^0$ and 45^0 as follows:

Spread at 4·5 m throw for: $22·5^0 = 2·3$ m
Spread at 4·5 m throw for: $45^0 \quad = 3·9$ m

The difference between the two angles being $22·5^0$, and represents a difference in spread of 1·6 m.

The additional spread required is 0·1 m, so the calculation becomes:

$$\frac{1·6 \text{m}}{0·1 \text{m}} = 16$$

$$\frac{22·5}{16} = 1·4^0$$

Therefore, deflection required to provide satisfactory air velocity in the occupied zone is:

$$22·5^0 + 1·4^0 = 23·9^0, \text{ say } 24^0$$

References

BSRIA, *Rules of Thumb,* TN 15/2001, BSRIA 2001, ISBN 086022 587 9

Lawrence Race G, *Design Checks for HVAC – A Quality Control Framework for Building Services Engineers* – sheet 46, AG 1/2002, BSRIA 2002, ISBN 0 86022 589 5

See also:

Sheet C1 Internal heat gains
Sheet C3 Cooling plant loads
Sheet C4 Ventilation – Fresh air requirements
Sheet C5 Supply air quantity and condition
Sheet A5 Duct system – Index Run

DESIGN WATCHPOINTS

1. Make sure that the grille meets all the criteria required, including throw, velocity, noise level and pressure drop.

2. Where applicable, check grille/diffuser performance is satisfactory under both heating and cooling modes. The performance may vary as the air volume and/or temperature changes.

3. Check that the air velocity in the occupied zone is acceptable.

4. Check that the grille/diffuser is compatible with the ceiling system if applicable.

5. Check that the grille selected can fit in the space available, including the addition of any plenums or grille boxes that may be required.

6. Size grilles and diffusers to ensure adequate spread and air movement throughout the whole of the area being served.

7. When considering a grille or diffuser type for sizing, consider the air pattern required. Fixed blade devices will not always be suitable for use in areas with low ceiling heights.

8. Check manufacturers recommendations for the maximum duct velocities into plenum boxes.

9. When using long contoured ducting and flexible ducting and connections, the pressure drop can be increased significantly. Ideally keep to a minimum but be aware of the pressure drop it incurs.

10. Size devices to deal with local loads where possible. Often, dealing with a heat gain at source will improve air patterns throughout the space generally whereas a high local gain could disrupt airflow.

A8   AIR DENSITY CORRECTION

Overview
Density is defined as mass per unit volume; it varies with altitude and temperature. The units of density are kg/m^3.

(The standard value normally used for density is 1·2 kg/m^3 at 20°C dry bulb, 1013·25 mbar)

Note that 1 bar = 1000 mbar = 10^5 Pa (100,000 Pa) = 100kPa. Standard atmospheric pressure: 1 atm = 1·01325 bar.

Barometric pressure changes with altitude. At altitudes above sea level it reduces from the standard value of 1013·25 mbar. For example Nairobi, which is at a height of 1820 m above sea level, has a standard atmospheric pressure of 776 mbar.

From the general gas law, density changes with pressure. Therefore the higher the altitude the lower the density of air. This affects the volume flow rate of air conditioning systems. Mass flow rate remains unchanged, so as the density decreases the volume flow rate increases.

In practice, even at standard operating conditions, systems will operate at continually changing atmospheric pressure of between approximately 980–1020 mbar due to normal atmospheric pressure variations. Density will therefore vary slightly anyway. (See Design Watchpoint 1.)

As altitude increases the mass of O_2 in the air decreases (think of mountaineers). Air conditioning and ventilation systems will require more air to meet a certain performance at a high altitude than they would at sea level.

From the psychrometric tables in *CIBSE Guide C,* at 20°C dry bulb, 101·325 kPa the following densities have been determined from $\upsilon =1/ \rho$

μ % saturation	φ relative humidity	υ specific volume m³/kg	ρ density kg/m³
50	50·59	0·8399	1·1906
43	43·58	0·8386	1·1924
100	100	0·8497	1·1769
0	0	0·8301	1·2046

Density at a particular altitude can be found in two ways:

1. Knowing the atmospheric pressure at the new latitude, density can be found using the general gas law.
2. Using the density value at sea level as a reference value, a correction factor is applied to obtain the condition of the air at the altitude of the particular case being considered. Such factors are published in a variety of sources such as *Thermodynamic and Transport Properties of Fluids, Fifth Edition,* by G F C Rogers and Y R Mayhew.

Once the corrected density has been found, the corrected value can then be used for all calculations where density is an integral factor. (See Design Watchpoint 2.)

> **Design tip:** Density can vary with temperature without a corresponding change in pressure as shown in table 4.36, *CIBSE Guide A.*

Design information required
The altitude of the site in metres
The air density will vary with the altitude, and so knowledge of the altitude of the site under consideration is essential, particularly in more extreme or higher locations. Variation in a single building may also be relevant if the building is particularly tall.

The appropriate correction factor (for method 2)
The exact correction factor needs to be determined to suit the particular location in order to ensure that plant and systems are not undersized.

Calculation procedure I
Step I. Establish the altitude and atmospheric pressure of the site under consideration. This can be found from meteorological data, or from the site itself.

Step 2. Use the general gas law equation to calculate the revised density.

$$PV = mRT$$
$$\frac{m}{v}=\frac{P}{RT}$$

Where:
P = pressure
V = volume
m = mass
R = particular gas constant
T = absolute temperature (273 + t_a, t_a = air dry bulb temperature in °C)

$$\rho=1\cdot 2\times\frac{P_{at}(273+20)}{1013(273+t_a)}$$
$$\rho=0\cdot 347\times\frac{P_{at}}{(273+t_a)}$$

Where:
t_a = air dry bulb temperature in °C
P_{at} = atmospheric pressure

Example I
Step I. Calculate the corrected density value for air which has a temperature of 27°C and an atmospheric pressure of 885 mbar.

Step 2. Using,

$$\rho=0\cdot 347\times\frac{P_{at}}{(273+t_a)}$$
$$\rho=0\cdot 347\times\frac{885}{(273+27)}=0\cdot 347\times\frac{885}{300}=1\cdot 024 \text{ kg/m}^3$$

A8 AIR DENSITY CORRECTION

Calculation procedure 2

Step 1. Establish the altitude of the site under consideration. This can be found from meteorological data, or from the site itself.

Step 2. Interpolate the exact correction factor from published data source.

Step 3. Multiply the density value at sea level (1.225 kg/m^3) by the correction factor to obtain the corrected density value.

Example 2

Calculate the corrected density value for the following site (correction factors used from *Thermodynamic and Transport Properties of Fluids, Fifth Edition, by G F C Rogers and Y R Mayhew*).

Design data
Location: Mexico City, Mexico
Altitude: 2234 m

Step 1. The altitude of the site is 2234 m above sea level, as detailed in table 2.18 of *CIBSE Guide A*.

Step 2. Interpolating between the correction factors for 2000 m and 2500 m to get the exact value for 2234 m:

Correction factor at 2000 m: 0.8217
Correction factor at 2500 m: 0.7812

$$0.8217 - 0.7812 = 0.0405$$

$$0.0405 \times \frac{234}{500} = 0.0190$$

$$0.8217 - 0.0190 = 0.8027$$

Step 3. So, the corrected density becomes:

$$1.225 \times 0.8027 = 0.9833 \, \text{kg/m}^3$$

Example 3

Calculate the corrected density value for a site with an altitude of 2000 m (correction factor used from *Thermodynamic and Transport Properties of Fluids, Fifth Edition, by G F C Rogers and Y R Mayhew*).

Step 1. The altitude of the site is 2000 m above sea level.

Step 2. The correction factor for 2000 m = 0.8217

Step 3. So, the corrected density becomes;

$$1.225 \times 0.8217 = 1.0066 \, \text{kg/m}^3$$

Example 4

Calculate the corrected density value for a site with an altitude of 2500 m (correction factor used from *Thermodynamic and Transport Properties of Fluids, Fifth Edition, by G F C Rogers and Y R Mayhew*).

Step 1. The altitude of the site is 2500 m above sea level.

Step 2. The correction factors for 2500 m = 0.7812

Step 3. So, the corrected density becomes:

$$1.225 \times 0.7812 = 0.9570 \, \text{kg/m}^3$$

Rule of Thumb Data

At habitable altitude, the rate of reduction can be taken as 0.1 mbar per metre of height above sea level and an increase of 0.1 mbar per metre depth below sea level.

References

CIBSE Guide A, *Environmental design*, 1999
ISBN 0 900953 96 9
G F C Rogers and Y R Mayhew, *Thermodynamic and Transport Properties of Fluids* – fifth edition, 2001, ISBN 0 63119703 6
Roger Legg, *Air Conditioning Systems; Design, Commissioning and Maintenance*, 1991, ISBN 0 7134 5644 2

See also:

Sheet H8 Boiler sizing
Sheet H9 Flue sizing
Sheet C5 Supply air quantity and condition
Sheet C6 Battery sizing
Sheet A6 Fan sizing

DESIGN WATCHPOINTS

1. Correction of air density is important. When comparing density at sea level (1.225 kg/m^3 at 1013.25 m bar, 15.15°C) and density at 2,000 m above sea level (1.0066 kg/m^3 at 795.0 m bar, 2.2°C), the density has decreased by nearly 18%. When compared to air density at 2,500 m (0.9570 kg/m^3 at 746.9 m bar, -1.1°C) the decrease in air density is nearly 22%.

2. Using the incorrect density values for a site can have a serious effect on the performance of the equipment.

© BSRIA BG 30/2003

A9 PRESSURISATION OF SPACES

Overview

Consideration of pressurisation is part of ventilation system design. Spaces or zones may require pressurisation (either positive or negative with respect to surrounding areas), for a variety of reasons ranging from containment of contaminants to maintaining clean room conditions for manufacturing or in hospitals.

An example is shown below of positive pressurisation of a hospital operating theatre. The pressure in the operating theatre is higher than the pressure in the connecting scrub room. That, in turn, has a room pressure that is higher than the entrance lobby. This will reduce the risk of airborne contaminants entering the operating theatre.

| Operating theatre +20Pa | Scrubs room +10Pa | Entrance lobby + 0Pa |

Sources such as the *NHS Estates Guides* and *BS 5588 Part 4* give calculation procedures for achieving these types of room pressure arrangements.

Positive pressurisation

In this case the room is kept at a positive pressure by supplying more air to the space than is extracted, thus providing a flow of air out from the space. This reduces the risk of airborne contaminants entering the space. Typical applications are:

- Operating theatres, to avoid contaminating the sterile environment
- Manufacturing processes, to prevent contamination of the products
- Means of escape corridors, this may be required by the local authority to ensure a smoke free escape route.

Negative pressurisation

This is the reverse of the previous situation. Here more air is extracted than supplied, resulting in a flow of air into the room from surrounding spaces. This reduces the risk of airborne contaminants entering surrounding spaces. Typical applications are:

- Nuclear processing, to prevent leakage of contaminated air
- Toilets, to stop the vitiated air escaping into surrounding areas, and control odours
- Catering kitchens, to prevent moist and odorous air getting into other areas.

To maintain a space at the desired level of pressurisation requires careful design of the ventilation systems. The pressurisation within each space is generally referred to as a differential pressure (Pa) between the space and surrounding areas. For example, an operating theatre may be kept at a positive pressure of +10 Pa compared to the scrubs/sluice room next to it, and +15 Pa compared to the corridor.

> **Design tip:** It is useful to put pressurisation information on to air flow diagrams to help determine air patterns.

In practice, the rooms are usually arranged to provide a cascade affect, rising 5 Pa between rooms, with the greatest overall pressure level in the room requiring the highest level of cleanliness.

A reverse of the above pattern will be observed in negatively pressurised areas where the most heavily contaminated areas will have the largest negative pressure. This is particularly applicable to nuclear or some process applications where airflow under negative pressure is used to protect other working areas.

Design information required

Internal design criteria
Including required air quality.

The use of the space and details of any processes.
This is needed to determine the level of pressurisation required.

The building layout
Including space dimensions, relationship with surrounding areas, details of separation and zoning.

Statutory requirements
Many industries or applications have very particular standards for maintaining pressurisation gradients, such as the health service, and the nuclear industry. These will generally detail the requirements for the particular case.

Pressurisation levels
These may be determined by reference to the appropriate statutory document, or from more general design sources in less critical cases.

Details of other ventilation systems
That could have an impact on the area being pressurised. This is important to avoid system interaction and achieve the required control of air flow and hence pressure.

Design outputs

- Air flow diagrams illustrating air flow paths and patterns
- Required supply and extract rates to achieve required degree of pressurisation

Calculation procedure

In its simplest form, pressurisation can be expressed as a percentage difference between supply and extract air flows. For example, in order to maintain a negative pressure in a simple toilet area, the supply air rate may be specified as only 80% of the amount being extracted. The remaining 20% will be drawn from surrounding areas through transfer grilles or under doors.

A9   PRESSURISATION OF SPACES

Example 1

Calculate the supply and extract air volumes, and the supply air change rate for the following toilet area:

Design data

Space dimensions:

Length: 6 m
Width: 4 m
Height: 3 m.
(See Design Watchpoint 3.)

Ventilation rates:

Supply: 80% of extract
Extract: 8 air changes/hour.

To calculate the extract air volume

$$\begin{aligned}
\text{Room volume} \quad &= \text{length x width x height} \\
&= 6 \text{ m x } 4 \text{ m x } 3 \text{ m} \\
&= 72 \text{ m}^3
\end{aligned}$$

$$\begin{aligned}
\text{Extract air volume} \quad &= \text{volume x air change rate} \\
&= 72 \text{ m}^3 \text{ x } 8 \text{ ac/hr} \\
&= 576 \text{ m}^3/\text{h} \\
&= 0 \cdot 16 \text{ m}^3/\text{s}
\end{aligned}$$

If the supply air volume is 80% of the extract volume, then:

$$\begin{aligned}
\text{Supply air volume} \quad &= \text{extract volume x } 0 \cdot 8 \\
&= 0 \cdot 16 \text{ m}^3/\text{s x } 0 \cdot 8 \\
&= 0 \cdot 128 \text{ m}^3/\text{s}
\end{aligned}$$

As an air change rate, this equates to:

$$\begin{aligned}
\text{Supply air change rate} &= \text{extract rate x } 0 \cdot 8 \\
&= 8 \text{ ac/h x } 0 \cdot 8 \\
&= 6 \cdot 4 \text{ ac/h}
\end{aligned}$$

References

Building Regulations
CIBSE Guide A, *Environmental design*, 1999, Section 1
ISBN 0 900 953 969
CIBSE Guide B2, *Ventilation and Air Conditioning*, 2001,
ISBN 1 903287 16 2
Lawrence Race G, *Design Checks for HVAC – A Quality Control Framework for Building Services Engineers* – sheet 8, AG 1/2002,
BSRIA 2002, ISBN 0 86022 589 5
BSI, BS 5588, Part 4: 1998 - *Fire Precautions in the Design, Construction and use of Buildings; Code of Practice for Smoke Control Using Pressure Differentials*, BSI 1998, ISBN 0580262424

See also

Sheet H5 Heat loss
Sheet H6 Plant heating load
Sheet H8 Boiler sizing
Sheet C4 Ventilation – Fresh air requirements
Sheet C3 Cooling load

DESIGN WATCHPOINTS

1. Excess negative pressure can result in increased heat losses through introducing more infiltration than was allowed for in the heat loss calculations.

2. Do not over-pressurise (or under-pressurise) a space, as there may be difficulty in using the area effectively such as doors being difficult to open or close, or keep closed once shut.

3. Use dimensions given on the drawings wherever possible rather than scaling-off. Drawings can distort during the copying process resulting in inaccuracies when measuring from the print.

4. In applications where air quality is important, check that the allowance for fresh air is sufficient to maintain the required air quality.

5. Where make-up air is required to replace air being extracted, check that the path for the make-up air is achievable. The use of an air flow diagram is a simple way to plot air paths and ensure that there is an airflow balance throughout the building that satisfies the design.

6. When designing pressurisation systems for means of escape, a path must also be provided for the air to leave the space, creating a flow of air at the stipulated velocity. This is a requirement of BS 5588 and is often forgotten.

7. When providing transfer air, make sure that the fire integrity is maintained between fire compartments.

8. Make sure that the required pressure in any particular area can be maintained as the operating conditions of other plant vary. A good example is where the air conditioning system is used to over-pressurise an office. If a variable air volume system is used, the return or extract air volume should be matched to the supply so that as the supply volume changes with internal conditions, the extract/return varies accordingly, thus maintaining the same pressure differential in the space.

ALPHABETICAL LIST

© BSRIA BG 30/2003